TOP

Chwedlau
ffestiniog
fables

By Peter Jarvis
with illustrations by David Charlesworth

**RHEILFFORDD
FFESTINIOG RAILWAY**

HARBOUR STATION, PORTHMADOG,
GWYNEDD LL49 9NF

1994

CONTENTS

RHEILFFORDD FFESTINIOG RAILWAY

The Ffestiniog Railway has been running through one of the most beautiful valleys of North Wales for well over 150 years, and unless you know differently, we think we have the oldest railway company still in business in the world, being formed by Act of Parliament on 23 May 1832.

Slate has been mined at the upper end of the Vale of Ffestiniog since Methusalem Jones dreamed of it in 1750: it was carried down to the sea by packhorse and boat in those days. The Ffestiniog Railway began to carry slate in 1836, and the first mention of tourist passengers seems to have followed in 1850, but this was an irregular business because other Acts of Parliament prohibited narrow gauge railways from carrying passengers. So the Ffestiniog Railway bought carriages and conveyed the passengers free, but charged for their hats, coats and umbrellas. The Board of Trade gave way and an officially approved passenger service began in 1865.

We used to run the slate trains downhill by gravity and haul the trucks back with horses (we still have the stables). In 1863 we began to use some of the smallest steam locomotives built up to that time (we have four of the original six - two are still working) and in 1869 we introduced the ancestor of all modern diesel and electric locomotives, having two swivelling power bogies with a power generator above them.

These curious push-me-pull-you double engines have almost been the trade-mark of the FR ever since: we still build new ones now and again.

We introduced bogie carriages to Britain in 1872 (we still have the originals in service) and it was not long before the larger railways followed our example (although for some reason they call their vehicles 'coaches'). We have been using petrol or diesel locomotives since 1923, which we think is longer than any other railway in the country. We still have a reputation for technical innovation, but we hope this does not spoil the old-fashioned appearance of our trains.

The FR is run by a core of some 30 permanent staff, supported by the Ffestiniog Railway Society which has over 5000 members of whom about a thousand are on our volunteer register.

Some families have been volunteering on the Railway for three generations.

If you like watching or riding little trains in glorious scenery, you should join the Ffestiniog Railway Society. You don't have to volunteer for work, but if you would like to be a guard, fireman, driver, signalman or buffet car attendant, or if you want to maintain the track or telephones, build dry stone walls or help with our station gardens, now is your chance to join us.

Why not join the Ffestiniog Railway Society?
Write to us at Harbour Station, PORTHMADOG, Gwynedd LL49 9NF.

4

Preface

The art of taking known facts and weaving a tale to account for them is exceedingly ancient: legends of this kind from at least two thousand years ago are still current in Wales. Some elements from early days may have crept into these tales; in particular, the stories of Merddin Emrys and Taliesin are substantially as I was told them at school. I owe a profound debt to those earlier writers Gildas, Nennius, Geoffrey of Monmouth, the chronicler of the Red Book of Hergest, Thomas Love Peacock and Lady Charlotte Guest. Without these illustrious predecessors, I could not have written this book.

However, other elements of more recent events have been embroidered and woven into the rich tapestry of local myth, Celtic twilight and all. Historians should beware!

The local tradition of verse is well-known, but perhaps the influence of the valley upon English-speaking writers is not so fully acknowledged. It would seem that most of the standard English poets or their close followers have visited the Vale of Ffestiniog and recorded their impressions: in this work we propose to give some examples.

Where living people have entered this book, they have expressed themselves happy with the result: therefore any resemblance to any other person is entirely coincidental and unintentional.

David Charlesworth has not only illustrated the stories but has also prepared the book for publication: it is a pleasure to acknowledge his collaboration. David Charlton took a most welcome initiative in encouraging us to publish our work.

I am grateful to the Editors of the Festiniog Railway Magazine (in which many of these stories and verses have previously been printed) for permission to republish them. I am also most appreciative of the assistance given by Michael Seymour, Archivist to the Festiniog Railway Company who has a most valuable fund of accurate information willingly offered.

Otherwise the work has largely been a family effort, and I am glad to acknowledge Hilary Jarvis' help, firstly for the use of her bedtime stories and secondly as co-author of one of them. I am grateful to Tony Conran for his help and encouragement with the *Hanes Taliesin*, and to my wife Sue who has been most helpful, especially in those almost lost techniques of craftsmanship in writing: grammar, syntax and spelling.

Most of the remaining errors and anachronisms are deliberate and are entirely my fault, but if any accidental mistakes remain, I offer my apologies in advance.

Peter Jarvis.

Little Wonder

Heron watching boy fishing,

Trout rising, line springing.

Coal siding, loco lazing;

Steps hurrying, fish gleaming.

Steam blowing, grate glowing,

Trout gutting, bread cutting,

Fish buttering, shovel clattering,

Fire fizzling, men guzzling.

merddin emrys

Merddin Emrys, or Myrddin Emrys as he is more usually spelt in modern Welsh, was the original of the wizard Merlin celebrated for his conjuring tricks in the films of the court of King Arthur. Myrddin has been noted for many centuries, but the further back one pursues him, the more shadowy he becomes. We have to reconstruct the tale as well as we can from often unreliable accounts by conflicting chroniclers, some of whom were writing down debased fragments of an oral tradition long centuries after the events in question, for the scene of Myrddin's activities was the darkest corner of Britain at the darkest time of the Dark Ages.

ortigern was High King of the Britons in the times after the Roman legions had left. He had to keep his eye on the petty kings of the various parts of the Island of Britain who would overthrow him if they could, and he had to watch that the *Dux Bellorum* - Constantine the Tyrant who was the military overlord - stuck to his job of keeping out Saxon invaders and didn't stick his sword in Vortigern's back. Eventually Vortigern arranged to have Constantine killed, and he would have killed the rest of the family too, but Constantine's son Aurelius Ambrosius, swearing vengeance, escaped to Brittany, leaving Vortigern to fend off the Saxons on his own.

Vortigern soon found he had not the forces necessary to repel the waves of Angles, Saxons and according to some obstinate historians the Jutes, so he invited some other Saxons, led by Hengest and Horsa, to do his fighting for him. He even married Hengest's daughter Rowena and gave half of Kent in exchange for her. However as is the way with overmighty subjects, they turned on him and expelled him so that he fled to the top left hand corner of Wales, to the Glaslyn valley.

There Vortigern began to build a fortress on top of the rock opposite the Sygun Copper Mine, and he started a splendid building over a pool on the top of the hill, but everything which was built in the day was knocked down in the night. Politicians tend to be as silly in one age as in another, and Vortigern sent for his astrologers to inquire why this should be so. They had no idea, but they feared for their jobs - and maybe their lives - if they could not produce an answer. So they said the unlikeliest thing they could think of, which was that the building would not stand unless it were sprinkled with the blood of a man who had no father.

Naturally no such person could be found in North Wales where everybody knows all about everyone else's family, but a young man was discovered in South Wales who answered the description perfectly. They brought him before Vortigern to be introduced.

'How d'you do, Myrddin,' said Vortigern. 'Now would you excuse us a moment while we kill you,' he added, 'and then if you don't mind, we'll just sprinkle your blood on these ruins.'

He was so reasonable about it that Myrddin ventured to point out that this would be a breach of the rules of hospitality: you don't cut someone you've been introduced to, still less when they are in your house.

'At least', said Myrddin, 'Perhaps you'd have the kindness to explain why?'

So Vortigern explained why, quite politely, because he didn't want a curse put on him. The curse of an innocent being always brings the worst of bad luck.

'Been listening to astrologers, have you?' asked Myrddin, shaking his head. 'No good will come of that. What you need is a consulting engineer: here, let me have a look.'

So Vortigern, always reasonable, led the way up the hill to the building around the pool. Myrddin took a long stick and poked in the water.

'There's a big stone in the bottom', he said. 'Your trouble is that there are two dragons under here. One is white, and one is red: each night they come out and fight for the supremacy of the island of Britain. If the red one wins, then the Britons will beat the Saxons, and if the white one overcomes the red, then the Saxons will rule over the Britons. We could run a book on it, if you like,' he added thoughtfully, for he knew that Vortigern was a man who loved a wager.

'Done!' cried Vortigern, the thought of blood put from his mind for the moment. 'Come and have dinner, then we'll watch the pool afterwards. Tell you what - if you're right and the dragons come out, we'll slit the throats of the court astrologers instead!'

Roaring with laughter at his own humour, Vortigern led the way down the hill again. The astrologers didn't feel like dinner in the least little bit, and indeed by the time it was served they were five miles away up the mountain paths on their ponies. Myrddin was a little dry in the mouth but he ate his dinner as well as he could, though he had to wash it down with the excellent hill water from a great horn put in front of him. He didn't fancy the beer: he had to keep a clear head.

Dinner was not quite finished when there was a fearful rumpus from the hill - steam and smoke and hissing and squeaking, with occasional bellowing and flashes of flame. The dragons could be seen breaking cover from their smoke screens and pouncing on each other with some very bad language like a pair of pussycats having a disagreement. Everyone kept quiet and put their hands over their ears until the row reached a climax and with a great cloud of water vapour, the dragons sank back in the pond. You couldn't see who'd won for the steam, but the damage to the day's masonry was only too evident. The cries of Vortigern calling for the heads of the astrologers and the distracted replies of the courtiers that no astrologers were to be found, that they had disappeared magically in a puff of blue smoke and that plainly Myrddin was the man to ask, gave Myrddin time to collect his thoughts.

'Right,' he announced firmly, 'tomorrow the same thing will happen, but we shall be ready. Have you a barrel of beer? or even better, mead?' because, as you know, dragons have an incurable taste for sweet things. A nine-gallon barrel of mead was produced. Myrddin sampled it. It was good.

'Splendid,' he declared. 'We shall put this out tomorrow with a linen cloth over it, or even better a big silk scarf. Have you....?' and silk scarves were waved in profusion.

'The dragons will come out and fight,' he said, 'then they will get thirsty and drink all the mead. Then they will get tied up in the silk scarf and fall asleep in the bottom of the barrel. Then you should knock the top onto the barrel and put it under the big stone in the bottom of the pool, while they are asleep. Then you can build your castle. I will send my account in due course.'

Naturally all these things happened just as Myrddin said, and his fortune was made. The hill has been known as Dinas Emrys to this day and odd things still happen there. People paid close attention to his prophecies as long as he lived (and cheerfully added to them well into the eighteenth century): in particular, once he was safely out of Vortigern's reach, he prophesied the overthrow of that despot at the hands of Aurelius Ambrosius who duly returned from Britanny and fulfilled the prophecy. Myrddin thereafter had a job for life as bard and prophet for Aurelius: he added his new chief's second name to his own and thus became Merlinus Ambrosius, or Myrddin Emrys in Welsh.

A collection of Welsh sayings known as the Triads mention Myrddin Emrys as one of the Three Christian Bards of the Island of Britain. Of the other two, one is our old friend Taliesin. The other was Merlinus Caledonius Sylvester or Myrddin Wyllt who lived in Scotland: he received a head injury at a particularly nasty battle in 573 A.D., after which he retired to the woods and recited his poetry to pigs, whom he said (very likely correctly) were more appreciative of the finer things of life than were men.

In later times Merlin was credited with all manner of marvels, from the transport of the stones of Stonehenge from Ireland (it is very odd that they did indeed come from that direction - from Preseli in Pembrokeshire) to 'the wonderful Success of a Project now on Foot to make the River from the Severn to Stroud....navigable' in 1776!

The birth of King Arthur is a celebrated tale; by then Myrddin must have been becoming middle-aged. King Arthur may have lived from about 470 to 530 A.D. There are many stories about Myrddin's end: one especially appealing account is given in the Triads, where the Three Losses by Disappearance of the Island of Britain include 'Myrddin the bard of Aurelius with his nine scientific bards who went to sea in a boat of glass and there have been no tidings whither they went'. Another says he and his followers sleep on Bardsey, awaiting the return of Arthur. Another says that before he left Dinas Emrys for the last time, he buried there his golden chair, where it still remains.

Nobody paid much attention to Dinas Emrys until this century, but excavations there have shown dramatically how the account of the pool with the building by it, just as they were described in the chronicles, was essentially correct. They also found one of the earliest pieces of Christian pottery ever discovered in Britain, thus confirming the Triads, but they didn't find the golden chair.

One fine summer night I was talking over a glass of wine to the archaeologist in charge of the excavation.

Had he looked in the pool? I asked.

Yes, he had, and there was a great flat stone at the bottom of it.

Had he thought of looking underneath?

He nodded. Why hadn't he, then?

He looked carefully right and left, then took a pull at his glass.

'Didn't want to disturb the dragons', he said.

An engyn was ther alsoe, *Prins* hys nayme
Fro auntient Englaunts werkè cayme.
Yn Londonne was hee form'd but rays'd yn grace
Yn Caumbria he found hys place.
Hys myghtye wayne by thirty horses towwid
With new Mechanikon for lumbriyying loadde,
From Arfon gaer to Betws Garmon stepe
Past Pitts Hedde through ye Aberglaslyn depe
Atte length to Eifionydhs mirrord vayles
And Madawgs port to fynde hymselfe some rayles.
Heer werkèd hee a centurie or soe
Tyll lekynge boyler tubbis and fumys fro ffyreboxe blowe.
Hys starting ryvettis claunkys and knokkys belowe
Betrayeth to al that Pryns wil not muche farther goe.
Brynge Spanres, Hamres, Toules of al traddys sende
ffor strenge and learnèd men our Prynce must mende
And they yt labour not, brynge shekels hither, since
Ye leste yt ye can doe ys pay your pount ffor Prynse.

Extract from 'The Seyntes Waie to Bardsey',a collection of pilgrims' tales ca.1450.

Glossary

Spanre, spaunre = long tool for separating or closing together 'nuttys' and 'boltis', q.v.
Hamre, hammre = a 'Brummagem tournscrew'. yt = that

The Afangc in Hafodllyn

There is certainly something curious about the Welsh mountains. Apart from such visible improbabilities as the Devil's Kitchen, wild goats and double Fairlies, a sympathetic ear to local storytellers will hear reliable accounts of those who have seen fairies on their way home after closing time on St. David's Day, and older legends about the Men of Harlech chasing maidens backwards across Migneint, or Will Davies chasing Princess backwards across the Cob. One of the more reliably documented stories is that of the afangc in Hafodllyn.

he afangc is a well-known Welsh breed of water-monster of great size and colossal strength, and it is great sport angling the beast. 'Over the years' says an old account,'there have been more anglers taken than afangc'. An afangc was hauled out of Llyn yr Afangc near Betws y Coed in the thirteenth century by means of two oxen and a chain, and another was taken from the Llynnau Diwaunedd on the south side of Moel Siabod in this century, but a proper account is hard to come by, possibly on account of the nature of the bait. You see, the afangc will eat only fair-haired blue-eyed virgin girls; as most of the Welsh have dark hair, bait is difficult to find.

The afangc in Hafodllyn first came on record in 1869, when it came out of the lake and snatched two passengers from the platform at the adjacent station.

14

A second visit in 1871 so alarmed the railway company that they moved the station to Tan y Bwlch in 1872. This was the last to be seen of the afangc until 1879, when the monster ambushed a short Up train headed by No.3, *Mountaineer*. It ate the engine (only the brass bell survived), the driver's girl (who was on the footplate) and three serving wenches whom it dragged out of the 'Servants and Luggage' compartment of No.15, the leading coach. After this, the company barred all the windows, locked all the carriages and installed elephant hooters on the engines, which are sounded to this day at Whistling Curve to frighten the afangc, though few could tell you why.

The fatal and repeated nature of these exploits encouraged G. Percy Spooner to devise a way of capturing the beast, so one morning he set forth with No.7 *Little Wonder*, an anchor and chain from one of the schooners, and Netta, his father's housemaid. When they arrived at Hafodllyn, Percy tied one end of the chain to No.7, and having secured the anchor end to Netta, he threw her in the lake. The afangc came across the lake like a torpedo and instantly swallowed her. In the words of an old account, the afangc 'turned to a display of the most singular ferocity'. Nearby villages, we are told, were swamped in a tidal wave, and avalanches fell into the lake from surrounding mountains. Percy Spooner, pulling on the other end of the chain with No.7 was barely able to hold his own with 240lb. on the clock. The boiler plates were spurting steam between them and the air was filled with the noise of steam and water. Percy edged inch by inch down the line to Whistling Curve, and the afangc came after him, thrashing down trees with its tail. Now, almost in his moment of triumph, Percy found out the fatal weakness of the Fairlie design: one of the ball and socket joints blew. The pressure dropped, the afangc made a tremendous leap in the air, broke the chain and fled back to the waters of Hafodllyn with the anchor and Netta lost inside it.

So that is why you find the succinct record quoted that Little Wonder was condemned, and why her boiler had lasted only ten years.

C. E. Spooner of course was most put out. He was not the sort of man to worry unduly about the bait, but he was very wroth about No.7. When Percy approached his father with a scheme to build a quadruple-bogie locomotive to catch the afangc, he was packed off forthwith to India.

As for the afangc, it has not been seen from that day to this. The company still takes precautions to ensure the safety of its passengers, but if you know anyone who fits the description of the bait, I would advise her not to go swimming in Hafodllyn.

To a Locomotive, lent to the York Railway Museum

Farewell, you are too dear for our possessing,
And like enough you know the Estimate
For your repair, in boilerwrights' assessing
Costs in needful parts in Tube and Plate.
While cylinders, too heavy for our Rails
Will each need Pony-trucks to hold their Weight,
Antipodean height of Cab entails
Some lowering, before you haul your Freight.
So stand aside in distant Yorkshire's vale,
Exhibited, a while in Exile bound;
Yet think, one day on sixty-pound new Rail
Your Whistle past Maentwrog may resound.
    With Blaenau reached, and Garnedd opened wide
    You should once more Ffestiniog metals ride.

THE DRAGON
at Pen Cob

Dragons are an essential part of Welsh lore. They have been well described as 'cunning, inquisitive, well armoured but not overbold'. They have their uses, even in bedtime tales.

 nce upon a time there was a little green dragon called Caradoc. He lived in the Gwydyr Forest on the hills above Betws y Coed with his mother and his father, and they ate snails and frogs, or mice if they could catch them. They had to hide in holes in the ground, because men kept tramping over the hills planting trees, but by and by the trees began to grow and the men came less often. The forest grew bigger and bigger and the little dragon found that you could walk all afternoon without coming to the end of it. Of course the frogs and mice grew bigger too, so the little dragon was able to catch as many as he liked, and he grew ever so big and strong. When he grew older, he found that his breath became hot and that he could cook the mice and frogs with his breath. This was something his mother and father had never done so well, because they hadn't grown so big and strong as Caradoc, but if you have ever tried to eat raw frogs, you will know why the little dragon liked them much better fried.

The little dragon grew and grew, and instead of the dull green which his father and mother had always been, he began to change colour - first to brown and then to a gorgeous pillar-box red. He began to sprout wings from his shoulders and although they were clumsy for flying about beneath the trees, they did very well to fan the fire when he was cooking his meals. The trouble was that sometimes he would set the forest on fire - he didn't mean to, you understand; it was just that his breath was so hot. Then the men would come and beat out the fire with big brooms and sticks and the little dragon had to hide in the bushes. However careful he was with his cooking, he sometimes had a

17

fire and the men came trampling all over the forest and made it very difficult for the dragons to live there.

One day, the little dragon's father took him on one side and said 'My boy, you have grown bigger and stronger than any of your family has done for years. We are very proud of you, Caradoc, but you have grown so big and you start so many fires that it is too exciting in the Gwydyr Forest with you here, so we think it is time for you to stretch your wings and seek your fortune in the Wide World.'

So the little dragon said good-bye to everyone and went all the way to the edge of the forest. From here he could see the rest of the Wide World, and it was a valley with some mountains on the far side. He flew off, flapping his wings and sticking his tail straight out behind to steer him.

He flew from Miners' Bridge to Manod and from Manod down to Maentwrog, where he came to a river winding down to the sea. There were steep hills on either side of the river and Caradoc flew into a wood on the sunny side of the valley. Near the top of the wood he found a big stone wall with lots of holes in it, so he crept inside and settled down.

The next morning he woke up and looking out of the hole in the wall, he saw steam coming through the wood.

'Goodness,' he thought, 'it's another dragon!' but it wasn't. He heard a noise, uffa chuffa, uffa chuffa, and round the corner came *Linda,* her brass dome shining in the sun and a row of carriages wobbling along behind, ding, dang, tinkledy bang. The little dragon thought this was a splendid sight and he breathed so hard with excitement that he started a fire. He didn't mean to, you understand, it was just because his breath was so hot. He did his best to put it out, but it was no good and he was getting rather worried when he heard the train coming back. Didong, didong, didingydongdong - it came round the corner and stopped. People got out of the train and put out the fire while the little dragon hid and watched. There was an argument between the two men who got out of the cab, each saying the other must have thrown cinders out of *Linda's* chimney. Caradoc's face went very red, but he kept quiet and presently, uffa chuffa, uffa chuffa, the train went away again.

The little dragon often went up and down the railway looking for rabbits to eat. Sometimes he started other fires - he didn't mean to, you understand, it was just because his breath was so hot. He found that every time, the people who came to put out the fires said 'Bother those engines!' and I am sorry to say he became a little careless.

One day he met a sheep on the railway and he ate it all up, roasted. It was really too big for one meal, and it gave him tummy-ache. As Caradoc sat in the shade by the wall, he saw a shepherd looking for the sheep: he was hunting all along the rails and nearly fell into an old mine shaft which he tried to peer down. The little dragon hiccupped, but the shepherd was saying 'blydi beirianau' (that means 'bother the engines' in Welsh) and didn't hear him. Caradoc's face was very red, but he kept quiet and presently the shepherd went away again.

This made the dragon decide to move further down the railway and one night he went all the way to the seashore. After he had eaten a big meal of fried fish early in the morning, he was looking for somewhere to sleep, when he peeped round the corner of a shed and saw the railway engines in their yard. He could see a pair of bedroom slippers sticking out of a cab, and after a lot of huffing and puffing noises, a breathless man in a dressing gown and a railwayman's hat scrambled out.

'I can't get the fire lit,' he said. 'The engine must be sulking.'

Another voice replied: 'Nonsense!' it said. 'You can't have swept the tubes out properly!'

While they were arguing, the dragon crept up to see what was happening. He looked in the firebox and saw a pile of cotton waste and wood.

'I could light that,' he thought, so he hooshed a great hoosh of hot breath into the firebox. There were flames all over the place, the fire lit and the engine started to boil just like that. The two men got such a dreadful surprise that they jumped right out of their slippers.

When they found Caradoc in the cab, they wondered whatever they were going to do. At last a man who was mending a carriage came and looked at him.

'Well,' he said, 'he's a lot better at lighting fires than you are, so why don't you ask him to stay?'

So they asked the dragon to come and live with them. At first they were going to let him live in the gunpowder shed, but they changed their minds in case he blew it up. They said, perhaps he'd rather live in the smithy and sleep in the fireplace, so his breath went up the chimney.

So that is how Caradoc the Dragon came to live at Pen Cob, and how he became a Useful Dragon. He gathers wood in the forest by the engine shed every morning and lights the fires to save the men from getting up so early. And as far as I know, they all lived happily ever afterwards.

PRINCE

I neuer saw that you did Paynting need,
And therefore to your Parts no Peynting set
Bvt vndernethe, your Motion must exceed
Your rvsting Tender in the Fitter's debt.
So therfor I haue serch'd and made Report
On all those Parts still extant which may showe
Some hope of future Service - to be short
Of bearing Brasses whych now Oyl-less goe,
Excentricks on their Axle wronglie plac'd
Of back-end Slapp and leaky Firebox Stays
Of Tubeplates to be ferrul'd and refac'd
And worn wheel tredds whose welded tyres amaze,
For Fytters to employ mechanick Arts
To make in Summe, a Whole of all your Parts.

Wm. Shakspaw
Boiler Inspector

THE FAY BRIDGE DISASTER

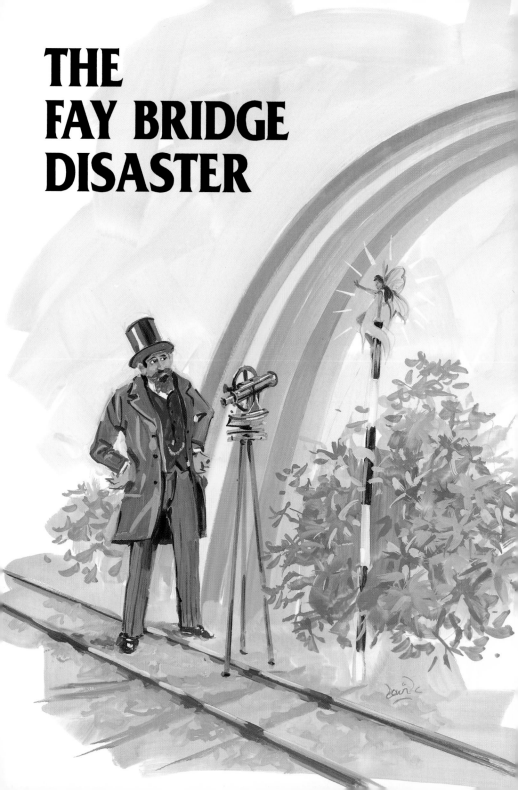

Welsh bridges often have odd stories about them, and this holds true from the Devil's Bridge near Aberystwyth to the new bridge at Conway. The Tan y Bwlch bridge is no exception. You will know that it has on it the inscription Boston Lodge Foundry 1854, and the story of why this was built nearly twenty years after the rest of the railway is one of the most curious in the history of the line.

t is well known that Wales is full of fairies and like beings. One of the most powerful wizards of all time, the great Merddin Emrys (the English call him Merlin), lived near Beddgelert, and the author of the oldest surviving British magical poetry, Taliesin, was Welsh too. There have even been platelayers on the railway who would not leave the woods on a fine day, lest people should see they cast no shadow.

Once upon a time there was a fairy called Elen, and she lived in a rhododendron flower on the Plas estate. She lived off honey brought to her by Will Jones' bees, and drank milk left for her at farmhouse doors. If she fancied anything a bit stronger, well, she could always go and help with the washing-up at the Oakeley Arms.

One day she was cooling her feet in Llyn Mair when James Spooner came in sight with his compass and measuring chain. Elen magicked a cup of tea from nowhere, and James sat down to drink it.

He wanted to build a railway across the valley, he said, but he was puzzled to know how. Even the new Menai Bridge which the great Telford had built would not have reached from one side of this valley to the other. Elen grinned. 'Leave it to me,' she said. 'The fairies can do better than that.'

She stood up and recited an ancient spell in Old Welsh - the sort of Welsh full of Vs and Ks, things which we are told don't exist in Welsh any more. The sky grew dark and presently, when it cleared away, James looked up and there, across the valley, with one end resting on the hill by Short Tunnel and the other in the trees by Tyler's curve, was a beautiful rainbow.

Of course, the rainbow had disadvantages. For some years, the trains ran with one of those timetable notes so dear to the heart of the Festiniog Railway management: the reason will be clear to those who know how rainbows work. 'Note E,' it said. 'Will run only on Fine Summer Evenings at Portmadoc when it is raining at Ffestiniog.'

After a while, the congestion became impossible, so Spooner went to talk to Elen. 'Well,' she said, 'if you want the trains across more often, you must think of me; it will rain in Ffestiniog, the rainbow will light up, and the train can come across.' So after this, when James thought of little Elen with her brown wizened face, her skinny legs and her shrill voice, all these things happened and worked very well so long as James remembered to think about Elen when Up trains reached Tyler's, or when Down trains reached Short Tunnel.

It would be pleasant to say that the railway company still ran trains across the rainbow, but alas, one day James met another fairy in the woods. This one was called Eirwen, and she sat reading an article in *The Red Dragon* on 'Give back Ffestiniog its second F!' As James sat drinking the tea she had magicked out of nowhere, admiring her raven locks, her complexion of peaches and cream, her soft voice and her very shapely person, he heard a tremendous noise of smashing slate from Tyler's - he had forgotten to think of Elen in time for the Up train.

So this is why the diversion was made, with its bridge dated 1854. Proof is to be seen over the edge of the embankment below Tyler's, on the Plas Estate, where you can see the broken slate from the accident.

Furthermore, even now, if you think hard enough about Elen, it will start to rain in Ffestiniog.

Jones! When east from Criccieth you and I
Set forth to trudge past mountain peaks and rills,
The long untrodden ways we wandered by
Among the waving leeks and daffodils.
Full weary were our blistered flatfoot toes
When came we down to gloomy Glaslyn's shore:
Beyond, the rocky height of Moelwyn rose -
We felt our feet could carry us no more.
When lo! the sound that whistled through the rain
The smoke that lazy curled, and steam that blew,
Behold that blessèd sight, a railway train
Which Blaenau-wards through hill and valley flew.
    With fresh-dried clothes, and rested feet restored
    It seemed but just, a pound for Prince, reward.

W.W. 'Yet more Lyrical Ballads'
ca. 1840 - 50.

THE GIANT'S FOOTSTEP

nce upon a time, Wales was not peopled by the little folk who placed their rails only two feet apart. We have it on the very best authority that there were giants in the earth in those days.

Giants were unpleasant people; they lived in huge hillforts with lines of ramparts around them: they terrorised the surroundings, chasing smaller folk with shaggy dogs the size of horses, and killing the young men who came to court their daughters. They had a reputation for being clumsy, uncouth and stupid. We have accounts of Ysbaddaden the Chief Giant who was so large that his eyelids had to be propped up on forks, and who threw poisoned spears at King Arthur's knights in so ineffective a manner that they caught the spears and hurled them back. The spears themselves seem to have been useless, for when Ysbaddaden had a spear through his eye, he remarked that in future his eye would be liable to water when he walked against the wind. Then there was Wrnach the Giant who had a magic sword - it was better than all the others because it was of iron - yet he looked after it so badly that he let it get blunted in his scabbard.

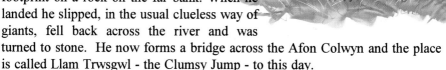

Among the legends about these fellows is the story of the two giants who had a jumping match by the Afon Colwyn above Beddgelert. One of them jumped from the main road right across the river, where you can still see his footprint on a rock on the far bank. When he landed he slipped, in the usual clueless way of giants, fell back across the river and was turned to stone. He now forms a bridge across the Afon Colwyn and the place is called Llam Trwsgwl - the Clumsy Jump - to this day.

The giants seem to have died out at the end of the Stone Age, and their disappearance appears to have been a great relief to everyone. For a long time, their memory was used only to frighten naughty children, but in the early 1920s when the giant had already been sleeping across the river for some thousands of years, McAlpine's burst upon the scene to build the notorious Welsh Highland Railway. The object of this exercise was to travel from Pitt's Head to Beddgelert by a route three times as far as by road, and on a gradient carefully calculated to pump dirty water out of the lower chimney of a Fairlie over the passengers, just to show how slow and dirty it is possible for a railway to be.

Inevitably, on their circular tour of the woods at Hafod Ruffydd, the railway came to the Giant's Footstep, and as the rock was in the way, the engineer wanted to put some gunpowder under it and blow it up. This proposal caused consternation among the local men of the construction gang, and as preparations proceeded, Welsh argument grew loud among them: eventually it became plain that they were about to go on strike. When the engineer asked 'Why?' they pointed to the stone bridge across the river.

'If you blow up the Giant's Footstep', they said, 'you will wake the Giant....'

In the end they did the safest thing. They diverted the railway to go round the side of the rock instead.

This story is pieced together from local legends of various origins. My thanks are due especially to the late Will Jones, whose crowbar marked McALPINE started it all.

Anyone doubting the truth of this tale is invited to go to Llam Trwsgwl at National Grid Ref SH575505 three-quarters of a mile south of Pitt's Head and to see the giant - and his footstep - for himself.

bran
A FRAGMENT

In Blaenau did the Blessèd Bran
Great Mines and Caverns there decree,
Where Fest, the sacred railroad ran
Through Tunnels measureless to man
Down to a sunlit sea.
So thrice five miles of hilly ground
With banks and cuttings there abound
And there were curves, all bright with sinuous rails
Where blossom'd many a rhododendron tree
Enfolding sunny spots of greenery.
But oh! that deep romantick chasm which slanted
Down the green hill from Tafarntrip!
A savage place, as hollow and inchanted

As e'er a liquor'd traveller took a dip;

And in this chasm, with ceaseless turmoil seething

As if the air in fast short pants were breathing

A mighty Fairlie momently with force

Five miles meandering with many a mazy motion

Amid the twisting trees has run his course

With steam and sound creating a commotion.

Through wood and dale the sacred railroad ran

Then reached the tunnel measureless to man

To sink in tumult in the lifeless lake.

Here the poet was interrupted by a person from Port Madock, and the rest of the noble work is lost to posterity.
From S.T.C.'s unpublished notebooks.

FUNNY OLD ENGINES

Bring on the Dancing Girls

nce upon a time, in a Sweet Little Valley in the Far Corner of Welsh Wales, there was a Dear Little Railway. The Fat and Thin Directors were the Oldest Railway Directors left in all Wales or indeed anywhere else, but they never let this worry them and their Funny Little Engines went up and down the Sweet Little Valley for years. As the Funny Little Engines grew older, some of them Fell to Bits or were sent to the Glan y Môr Yard at the Seaside to sniff the Salt Air, which came to the same thing. At last there were only three Funny Old Engines left. They were all Ever So Old and they had Funny Welsh Names like *Prince*; the others were called *Merddin Emrys* and *Taliesin*. They were all boys together and they used to sit in the Engine Shed making up Pennillion, which are a sort of Welsh Poetry, and watching the Welsh rain drip in through the roof.

One day a clergyman came to see them, and they were pleased to see him because in days gone by, a nice clergyman called Timmy had fastened up the Engine Shed so that people couldn't steal the Funny Old Engines, but that is a Different Story. This clergyman said 'I write books about Funny Old Engines, and please may I write one about you?'

Merddin looked him over with care and he seemed a Nice Clergyman, so he said 'Lots of People have written books about us, and you may write one if you wish, but you must be very careful when you draw our Pictures. You must not draw Faces on our Smokebox Doors. When I talk, I make noises out of my Chimney, and when I get very Steamed Up, I let off through my Safety Valves. When I look at you, I look out of my Spectacles. It would be Very Rude to make Noises out of my Smokebox Doors, and no Respectable Engine would ever do so. Anyway, I have Two Smokebox Doors, and if you drew a Face on one, whatever would you draw on the other?'

'Why is it,' asked the clergyman, 'that Prince looks at me with Round Spectacles, while yours are Nearly Square?'

'He looks at the Television too much!' interrupted Prince.

'Ah,' said Merddin, 'that's Culture, that is. Very hard it is when you have never been out of the Valley in your life, and the Telewele shows you the World Outside. Gives you Ideas, indeed.'

'Can I help with your Ideas?' asked the clergyman. 'Is there anything you would like from the World Outside?'

'Yes indeed,' replied the Funny Old Engines eagerly. 'Could you find us some Girl Engines?'

'Gracious!' said the clergyman, 'that's not my usual line! I usually marry people when they've already found a girl, you see.'

'Ah well,' said Merddin sadly, 'we'll remember that, in case. But you will watch out for some girl engines, won't you?'

So the clergyman promised and went away to write his book.

Benefit of Clergy

After this, the Funny Old Engines became Grumpier and Grumpier. Often they sulked and tried to get out of doing any work at all and at last the Fat Controller was very angry with them.

He said: 'I am getting Tired of Silly Old Engines who won't work, and if you can't do Better, I shall go and find some More Engines Somewhere Else!'

Merddin tried to answer back and had such a tantrum that he blew one of his firebox crown stays, so he had to be put at the back of the shed and couldn't do Any More Work at all. This meant that Prince had to pull Much Bigger Trains and he was most put out. All the way Up, he puffed 'I Shan't, I Won't, I Shan't, I Won't,' and all the way Down he chattered 'I'm Danged if I will, I'm Danged if I will,' until one day he tried to shake a piston rod with rage at the Fat Controller and managed to blow part of his Piston out of his Chimney, which gave him the most terrible Indigestion in his Valve Ports. While he was being mended, he saw the Fat Controller talking to the clergyman, and they left together to go over the mountains.

The Fat Controller returned looking very pleased about something but he didn't tell the Funny Old Engines why, so they had a great surprise when Another Engine arrived on the line.

She was rather dull to look at and she didn't think much of their track, screeching at every check-rail she met and sometimes jumping off the rails. The Fat Controller was cross, and he sent her into the works to be Altered. Taliesin was in the works too, so he got to know the new engine quite well, and as her alterations progressed, he came to like her even better. His liking was the more because she was a Girl Engine, and in her new coat of paint, from her scarlet crankpins to her gleaming green saddletank with its brass nameplate *Linda* she was every inch a Lady. To cap everything, she had every woman's crowning glory - a Gorgeous Golden Dome.

Taliesin was left in the Works. Linda went to see him often. Sometimes Merddin came too.

'Poor Tal,' he said, 'you do look a Mess with bits of you all over the erecting shop floor. But I feel quite jealous, because you have Linda to keep you company.'

'Never mind,' said Linda, 'My sister Blanche is coming soon, and I've told her

all about the Men in this place.'

This pleased Merddin very much, and when Blanche arrived, he was most attentive.

'What a Nice Big Strong Engine you are,' she said, 'would you like to come out double-heading with me?'

So they went out together and they got on splendidly, except one time when they went out to a party at the Thin Civil Engineer's house. They drank a nine-gallon barrel of his cider between them and rolled home Ever So Late.

"Where did you get to last night?' asked Merddin's driver in the morning. 'My mother was sitting up until two o'clock to open the crossing gates for you!'

That morning the clergyman came to see the engines again, and he met Linda in the yard.

'Psst!' she whispered, 'Did you say you fitted rings? You'd better take your overalls, because Merddin wants you to fit a new ring on Blanche.' So the clergyman went to the Engine Shed and did as he was asked. When he came out, all the other engines blew their whistles until they had no more steam left. Hearing a noise in the Engine Shed, Merddin's driver ran to see what it was, and he found Merddin and Blanche wrapped in steam with their safety valves lifting like anything.

'Funny,' he thought as he turned their blowers off, 'I wonder what's been happening here?'

But Blanche and Merddin winked at each other and said nothing.

The Blue Engine

The clergyman was talking to the Fat Controller. 'Have you any Blue Engines on your line?' he asked.

'No,' said the Fat Controller firmly. 'All our engines are Green Engines.'

And he drove Linda away to fetch the morning train.

Blanche stood sizzling on the ashpit. She felt tired.

'Can't understand it,' said her driver, scratching his head. 'Not steaming at all well, she isn't, yet there's nothing the matter that I can find. Just one of her off-days, I suppose'.'

But one off-day followed another, and Blanche became shorter and shorter of breath. She took to stopping in the woods so that the passengers could admire the view, and also to to get her breath back. Her coal bill became enormous.

'What's she playing at?' demanded the Fat Controller. 'She's eating enough coal for two engines!'

Blanche started to roll along the track with a peculiar Waddle and somehow she seemed Bigger. One day she was puffing and panting up the hill by the Cemetery when there was a Grinding Screech and she stopped suddenly.

'Ow,' she said, 'I'm Stuck!'

And so she was.

'This Cutting is too Tight for my Boiler,' she declared.

So Prince had to come and pull the train out of the cutting while all the passengers stuck their heads out between the bars on the windows.

'Blow my Fusible Plug!' said Prince. 'What are you doing, you Silly Fat Engine?'

Blanche burst into tears.

'I can't help it,' she cried. 'It happens to Girls, or how do you think the Company can provide for the Future?'

When Blanche arrived back at the Shed, her driver and the Thin Fitter went over her most carefully. They banged her wheels and shook her rods. They blew down her blastpipe and sucked out her tubes. They tried an Electronic Thing on her firebox stays. They undid her dome and listened to her boiler. Then they heard a Funny Noise.

'I can hear the clatter of tiny crankpins in here,' said the Thin Fitter. 'She must be expecting a Baby Engine!'

Then there was quite a Hullaballoo, and everyone made a great Fuss of her,

especially Merddin Emrys who was very proud indeed. He even pulled all her trains for her without a word of complaint, which for him was most unusual. Meanwhile Blanche sat in the Engine Shed and the clatter of her connecting rods became a familiar sound as she knitted a fibreglass jacket for the baby engine's boiler.

The Fat Controller was very silent when he heard the news. He went to his shelf, took down a large textbook on Advanced Locomotive Management and read a lot of small print until late in the night. The next day he said to Blanche's driver 'Call me when she starts Whistling,' and went away. This puzzled the driver until one evening he heard a little whistle in the Shed. Twenty minutes later, he heard another; twenty minutes after that he realised what was happening, so he and the Thin Fitter sent for the Fat Controller who soon arrived with a great bag of Spanners and Things.

'Put all the other engines out in the Yard,' he said, 'except Linda - she can Boil the Water.'

Night came and still the light was on in the Shed In the darkest part of the night, the Thin Fitter drove Merddin across to Portmadoc and back.

'What did he want?' asked a sleepy Prince when Merddin returned.

'More Boiling Water!' said Merddin indignantly. 'Often I have put Boiling Water in my cylinders for a Joke, but this is the first time I have been Asked for it!'

In the morning the clergymen came to see the Three Funny Old Engines, and he was surprised to see them outside in the Yard while such a lot of Steam and Noise came from the Engine Shed. Then the Fat Controller came out.

'We have a Baby Engine!' he announced. 'She weighs five tons, and Blanche only needed a couple of rivets in her foundation ring. Would you like to come and see?'

So they all trooped across to the Engine Shed and there they saw a much thinner Blanche and the nicest little engine you ever saw in Works Primer.

'What are you going to call her? What colour are you going to paint her?' asked the clergyman.

'You choose,' said Merddin and Blanche.

'All our engines are Green Engines,' muttered the Fat Controller, but the clergyman said 'I've always wanted to see a Blue Engine on your line, so she shall be Baby Britomart the Blue Engine,' and everyone cheered.

Afterwards the clergyman was talking to the Fat Controller.

'Would you have that all over again?' he asked. 'It must have been very tiring, sitting up like that all night.'

The Fat Controller considered for a moment.

'Oh, I don't know,' he said. 'As a matter of fact, I'm thinking of getting married myself.'

This story was originally written especially for the Rev. Mr. Wilbert Awdry, who expressed himself pleased with it. Acknowledgment is due to the late Mr. Francis Wayne in whose company, wall-building on the Deviation, the tale first took shape and who improved it afterwards in several delicate details.

The late Ken Sewell illustrated the original version of this story - we could not improve on his ideas so re-drew them for this edition!

To *mechanicks*
to make much of Tyme

Fettle your Fyrebox while ye may,
The future shows no clearer,
And that same Tube replaced today
Tomorrow will be dearer.
Therefore, while the gas is there,
And while ye may, go weld:
    Or that same Fyre whose flame ye spare
    May ever be withheld.

School of Herrick (1591 - 1674)

PALMERSTON
THE GHOST ENGINE

by Hilary and Peter Jarvis

The return to service of Palmerston *seemed an unlikely event in the 1970s, when his sale for scrap iron was narrowly avoided. Some inquiries as to why this should be have shown some very queer reasons, and their origins are to be found as usual in the doings of the Fair Folk and Otherworld People of these parts.*

ver the years there have been many battles fought in Arfon and Eifionydd by warriors invading the one from the other, and the ghosts have to go back every year for the anniversaries. In olden times this involved a long journey over the mountains along ghostly paths. but when the Welsh Highland Railway was built, it provided a far better means of travel. The ghosts found it very convenient because nobody else ever used the trains. As word of the ghosts spread among the humans of Nant Betws Garmon, the trains were used the less, and the spectral traffic increased. One of the Rural District Councils went broke because so much was spent on supporting the railway, so after that the Ghost R.D.C. had to help to pay for the trains, but as they could only pay in ghostly money which could only pay for ghost coal and ghost repairs, the trains became thinner and thinner until at last nothing could be seen of them at all. When the real rails were taken away, the Ghost R.D.C. paid for ghost rails, and ghost trains whistled in the Aberglaslyn tunnels at the usual times for years.

After the disappearance of the last W.H.R. ghost engine *Moel Tryfan* the ghost railway borrowed *Palmerston* to haul the ghost train. Poor old *Palmerston* was not very visible even then, and with the ghost repairs it had in the next fifteen years, you could see even less of it.

When *Palmerston* was threatened with a Bad End, the ghost railway wrote a letter to Allan Garraway which duly arrived by post, but as it was a ghost letter, of course he couldn't see it, so it stayed on his doormat. However ghost messages can make themselves felt in other ways and can make people do things without their knowing why: they just put it down to intuition, or never think of it at all. So everybody who trod on that doormat found good reasons for himself why *Palmerston* should not be scrapped, and very properly too.

The future looks satisfactory in that the Ghost R.D.C. councillors are condemned to meet every month in ghastly conclave to vote funds to pay for trains in all eternity. The ghost train still runs along the old W.H.R. and may be heard in the tunnel at 1301, 1501 and 1811 (Up to Porthmadog) and at 1114, 1429 and 1624 (Down from Porthmadog) at the right season of year, especially if there is a full moon.

But if we were you, we wouldn't go for a ride on it. You never know what battle awaits you at the far end.

THE WASTING TUBE

O Tube, thou art frail!
The invisible steam that flies in the wind
In the howling gale,
Has found out thy plate of secret rust,
And thy welded seam thinn'd
Takes thy fate on trust.

atelier of Blake
(1757 - 1827)

The influence of the F.R. extends not only to poetry but to music too. Verses, attributed respectively to William Blake (1757 - 1827) and Alfred, Lord Tennyson (1809 - 1892), see page 53, are justly celebrated for their settings by Benjamin Britten (1913 - 76).

The Moelwyn Gold Mine

North Wales is, or was, uncommonly rich in minerals. Apart from slate, coal, limestone and the granite which has been used to make everything from Stone Age axeheads to railway ballast, there are many metallic ores. Copper has been worked near Llandudno since the Bronze Age, and the Industrial Revolution had its origins along the March from Bersham to Coalbrookdale. Tin, manganese, silver and lead have all been worked at various times: the last craze was for uranium which was within recent years mined in the Gwydyr Forest above Betws y Coed. None of these however has quite the glamour of gold, which has been mined for three thousand years and which is still produced in small amounts near Dolgellau.

veryone has heard of the nineteenth century Gold Rush to Klondike; many know that the Colorado gold strike gave rise to an interesting series of narrow gauge railways, some of which still survive. Few people are aware that when the main line of the Cambrian Railways was built, gold was struck on Talerddig Bank; practically nobody has ever been told of the Moelwyn Gold Mine.

When the congestion on the Moelwyn Inclines became intolerable, about 1839, a contract was put out for tender for the construction of the notorious tunnel, and it was awarded to a wee man of the mountains. His name was Dillus the Bearded; he was a dwarf who in days gone by had made a living by hunting. One day while singeing a boar he had killed, he was knocked on the head by Sir Kay and Sir Bedivere who then twitched out his whiskers to make a dog-lead for King Arthur. After this indignity he went on a rehabilitation course to the Nibelungs who taught him to mine, to smelt and to fashion metals.

The contract specified that *'the tunnel shall be soundly mined....and built to a width of four paces and to twice the height of a well set-up fellow'*, but because of his own size, Dillus caused much trouble in future years to the

Ffestiniog Railway, for he built the tunnel only eight feet wide and barely nine feet high.

Halfway through the mountain, Dillus struck gold, so he very cannily took out the mineral rights on a 99-year lease and stayed on to extract the ore when the tunnel was completed in 1842. Water power was obtained from a small reservoir near the northern end of the tunnel, and Dillus worked happily for many years. He had at each end of the tunnel a special signal, rather like a disc distant but capped with square red plates instead of the more usual round ones. Under normal conditions the signals were left at Clear but when at Danger they denoted Blasting in Progress. The gold was kept in a bullion box and brought out of the tunnel each Friday on a trolley: Dillus then caught the Friday Evening Short train so that he could sell his wares to jewellers in Portmadoc on Saturday. At least one volunteer at Harbour Station in recent years wore one of Dillus' wedding rings.

The mine worked until the lease ran out in 1941. Dillus wished to renew the lease, but there was one of those furious disagreements which mar the story of the railway from time to time. The argument was because the railway had appropriated the Bullion Box for use as a Permanent Way Tool box, which function it still fulfils. Harsh words were spoken, and Dillus left in high dudgeon: as he went, he put a fearful curse on the tunnel he had built.

He swore by the Head of Bendigeidfran - a most powerful oath - that never again should the Ffestiniog Railway carry even one English tripper through his Moelwyn Tunnel.

Dillus the Bearded waiting for the Friday Evening Short. At left, his trolley. Centre, the Blasting in Progress signal. Right, Dillus leaning on the Bullion Box. Note that by measuring him from the scale of the rails at his feet, Dillus is only 4ft.7ins. high. Observe also that he casts no shadow on the lid of the box - this is a common finding among supernatural beings in these parts.

43

The recent discovery in a bank vault of a trunk containing verse by Percy Bysshe Shelley (1792 - 1822) reminds us that Shelley was one of the earlier volunteers working on the Festiniog Railway. It will be remembered that he rented William Madocks' house at Tan yr allt in the winter of 1812 - 13 and took a great interest in 'this great, this glorious cause', and that after an impassioned speech by him at Beaumaris on 28 September 1812 no less than £1,185 was subscribed, which ranks rather better than present day appeals if inflation is taken into account.

Like many enthusiasts, his enthusiasm was short-lived. There was some question of drug addiction and he left the district in some haste on 27 February 1813. It may also be recalled that his second wife Mary was a distinctly non-Railway wife who worked his enthusiasms out of her system by writing 'Frankenstein'.

Therefore it is with great pride that we present this hitherto unpublished sonnet, which has every appearance of being written by one of the foremost poets of the age.

I was a traveller in an antique land
And there, some vast and formless piles of stone
Like broken towers around the township stand
And huge deserted quarries stand, alone:
The wet reflecting roofs on every hand
Cry out that even Heaven Greaves and weeps.
In this deserted place, among these lifeless things
A small and ancient locomotive sleeps;
And on the pedestal these words appear:
'My name is *Princess,* born of England's kings:
Look on my works. Ye Friends of Earth, despair!'
No rails remain. A rotting signal waits;
For through the brooding moorland, bleak and bare,
Some day her *Prince* will pass the crossing gates.

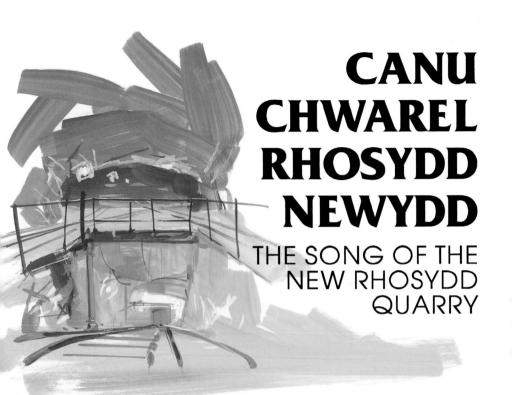

CANU CHWAREL RHOSYDD NEWYDD

THE SONG OF THE NEW RHOSYDD QUARRY

 early two thousand feet up Moelwyn on the pass between Cwm Croesor and Cwmorthin stands New Rhosydd Quarry. It is remote, often in cloud, and was the highest climb of any for the quarrymen who lived a thousand feet below at Tan y Grisiau. The only way up was by a sheep track between the cliffs, so steep that it was impossible to build an incline to let the loaded trucks down to Tan y Grisiau. Instead, the trucks were manhandled in the opposite direction over the pass to the head of Cwm Croesor. The tramway ran along a ledge which put the Ffestiniog's mountain climbing to shame, for the drop from the ledge into Cwm Croesor was a sheer six or seven hundred feet. At the head of the valley, the wagons were turned on a wagon turntable and let down the vertiginous New Rhosydd Incline at a gradient of rather more than 1 in 1 to the valley floor. From this comparative safety, threatened only by occasional avalanches, the trucks were hauled by horses along the Croesor tramway eight miles down the valley and across the Glaslyn marshes to Portmadoc, where they were usually transhipped to the Cambrian Railways at the Beddgelert Siding.

It seems that because of the violence of the gales at New Rhosydd, the quarrymen developed very strong lungs, and these they put to good use in their

choir. Every quarry had its own choir and the rivalry between them was intense: the quarrymen's eisteddfodau were well attended and hotly contested.

The tale goes that one year the Eisteddfod Genedlaethol - the National Eisteddfod - was held at Blaenau and New Rhosydd Quarry won the first prize in the Men's Choral competition. This is the realisation of any choir's wildest dreams, and no chorus in the land can do better. The exhilaration of the quarrymen knew no bounds and inspired them to contempt for the usual way of sending trucks down mere rails to Croesor. Men who could win First Prize in the Men's Choral at the Eisteddfod Genedlaethol were capable of greater things and nothing would content them but that they should instead take four loaded trucks - three tons each - home with them down the sheep track to Tan y Grisiau. They took strong ropes; with forty men to each wagon and singing that set the whole valley in echoes, they lowered the trucks a thousand feet down the mountainside to Cwmorthin. Having achieved this Herculean feat, they set them on the rails and awaited the effect of their crewling down the Cwmorthin incline to the Ffestiniog Railway at Tan y Grisiau.

The astonishment caused to the F.R. by the unexpected arrival of four Croesor Tramway wagons blandly bearing the destination note marked PORTMADOC (BEDDGELERT SIDING) is recounted with glee in the pubs of Blaenau to this day. It is given as an example of the power of music; as the reverend gentleman exclaimed: 'Praise the Lord, we're a musical nation!'

Benjamin Britten (1913 - 76) was also noted for his settings of traditional folk songs. It is not known at which local hostelry he can have heard the following railway ditty.

When I was a bachelor, I lived at the Lodge
And I worked in the wind and rain;
And the only only thing which I ever did wrong
Was to drive a Great Little Train.
I drove her in the autumn time
And in the springtime too,
And the only only thing that I ever did wrong
Was to keep from cornfield meetings in the dew.

Now that we are wedded it reminds me of the time
When I blew an awful gaffe:
You were riding on the footplate and I knew that I was wrong,
For I forgot the staff.
It reminds me of the autumn time
And of the springtime too -
And of your many many charms when I held you in my arms
Just to keep from cornfield meetings in the dew.

Glossary.

Cornfield meet = head-on collision in mid-section between two stations, an accident prevented by the 'staff' system.

The Mermaid of the Gomer Rock

Mermaids are widespread in North Wales, not only in the sea but in the rivers too. Their relations with humans are somewhat fraught, largely because of the wretched way humans treat them, catching them in fishing nets or disturbing their sleep with noisy motor boats. Some merfolk have taken to life ashore, as you will hear, and some have been quite happily resident at Plas Mawr in Conwy for many years.

Once a mermaid was washed up on the shore at Conwy, and asked a man to put her back in the water. Perhaps he was a ferryman - they had a reputation for bad manners, which is why Telford built the bridge - anyway, the nasty fellow wouldn't help the lady. So she died on the shore, and as she did so, she cursed Conwy, saying it would never prosper. It has remained in fair poverty to this day, which just shows, you have to be careful with mermaids.

Mermaids are quite well known on the F.R. Some longstanding volunteers will remember the time when a mermaid joined a working party in the late 1950s: you could tell she was a mermaid because she went swimming in the icy Afon Teigl in the dark, and enchanted Cledwyn Williams to hold a lantern for her. More, she went and did it again before breakfast - in February....

Another time, a merman came ashore at Pen Cob in the dark and fell onto the road, causing consternation among the constabulary. He had only come to see the Investiture of the Prince of Wales, being a loyal merman, and had lost his way. However there was a terrible fuss with the Navy and frogmen searching the harbour in case he was a Welsh Nationalist merman.

nce upon a time there was a mermaid called Myfanwy, and she sat on the Gomer Rock opposite Borth y Gêst singing and combing her hair. Some mermaids sing to attract the sailors and drown them, but Myfanwy was a Helpful Mermaid and she sang so that boats would not hit the Gomer Rock. In any case, if they did, it might spoil her underwater garden. Sometimes she went shopping, but this was a bit awkward because of her tail and she had to manage with what she could get at ships' chandlers as there weren't many other shops on the quay, but sometimes she would put on a long skirt and eat out at the Cob Café or the Sticky Spoon.

One day, *Lloyd George* was going across from Pen Cob to the Harbour to fetch his train, and just beyond Pen Cob junction, there was Myfanwy wriggling across the rails. Now *Lloyd George* was a large and powerful engine and not inclined to let things get in his way, but he had a weakness for a pretty face and as for a damsel in distress, well....he stopped. The driver got down.

'What *are* you doing?' he asked Myfanwy, who looked most uncomfortable.

'I'm going to see my aunt at Ffestiniog,' she said. 'I'm having to go this way because I can't get through the Harbour. The water there tasted awful,' she added.

'That's a nasty rash you've got,' said the driver, and so she had, all over her shining tail.

'Come on,' he said, 'I'll take you to see the First Aid Man.'

So the fireman held Myfanwy while the driver took them back to Boston Lodge, where the First Aid Man shook his head.

'Perhaps you ought to see the Company's doctors,' he said doubtfully, and off they went. There were three doctors: the first was very chatty and asked her all sorts of questions.

'Are you expecting, um, are you expecting eggs?' he wondered.

'Indeed, no,' replied Myfanwy sternly.

The second doctor hardly said anything but examined her very thoroughly: it isn't often you get a chance to examine a mermaid and it made his day, but he could find nothing to account for the rash.

The third doctor asked thoughtfully, 'Is there anything worrying you?'

'Only the nasty smell in the Harbour,' said Myfanwy. 'They empty the drains from Porthmadog onto the ebb tide, and it's horrible.'

'Ah', said all the doctors. 'Pollution,' they said. 'We must tell the E.C.'

'What's that?' asked Myfanwy.

'It's in Brussels,' said the doctors. 'It's in favour of small railways and against dirty rivers. We'll see what we can do. Meanwhile, how do we get you to Ffestiniog?'

'It's awkward on land; that's why we swim up and down the rivers,' Myfanwy replied. 'The Railway used to have a Salt Water Wagon for mermaids, but it rusted. Nowadays my aunt has a car to go to Blaenau; she likes shopping there in the wet. She goes ever so fast on her tail and a pair of crutches - it's quite as quick as walking.'

Myfanwy grinned. 'Auntie has a disabled sticker to park on yellow lines. She says you're nobody in Blaenau unless you've got a disabled sticker.'

They gave her some ointment for her rash, carried her up to Boston Lodge Halt and put her on the train for her aunt to collect at Blaenau. Then they wrote to the E.C. who agreed something would have to be done about the drains into the Harbour.

'For the moment,' the E.C. wrote, 'we are sending a grant to build a mermaid tunnel under the Cob.'

So that is why, if you look over the river just west of Pen Cob Junction when the tide is coming in, you can see the swirls from the mermaid tunnel. And you never know your luck; you might see the mermaid wave an arm as *Lloyd George* whistles to her.

If you would like to sponsor the restoration of the Mermaids' Salt Water Wagon, now in Minffordd Yard, please send your contributions to the Ffestiniog Railway Trust.

From The Prince
a Metrical Ode

The splendour falls on workshop walls
And ancient engines old and hoary,
As midnight oil may light the toil
Of grimed mechanics greased and gory.
   Blow, whistle, blow! round purple mountains flying,
   Whistle, blow! the horns of Elfland faint replying.

As coupled wheel rides shining steel
The dying sun a scene of slaughter,
As twilight fails, with grinding rails
Points yield as engines come for water.
   Blow, whistle, blow! set the wild echoes flying
   From Moelwyn's height the elvish sound replying.

Though Prince, put by, in pieces lie
His sparks and ashes gone to glory,
The purple hill is haunted still
His echo tells an everlasting story.
   Blow, whistle, blow! how clear, how well deserving
   The golden sound from all around of pounds for Prince
   preserving!

Alfred, Lord Tennyson (attrib.)

Crossing the Bar

y aunt lived at Borth y Gêst. She had a low house - I banged my head on her roof with horrid regularity - on the cliffs overlooking the Glaslyn estuary, and the view was one at which I never ceased to marvel. Perhaps it was at its most dramatic at a spring tide in the night time, with the black mass of Rhinog dominating the background and a full moon casting reflections like a silver road across the water from Talsarnau to the bottom of the garden, and the windbent branches of a bare tree silhouetted stark against the light. It was spectacularly beautiful and distinctly spooky.

One bright and cloudy morning I had gone out early into the garden: there was a strong ebb tide and a blustery southwest wind blowing hard enough into the bay to sting my cheeks and make me turn my head away. Down the river I could see the breakers on the treacherous Portmadoc harbour bar and became conscious of the sound, as of distant thunder. I reflected that more Portmadoc men had been drowned on their own doorstep than anywhere else in the wide world, and wandered about the garden: this was notable for a complete absence of roses - my aunt said there were plenty of flowers without trying those which bit her - but had splendid azaleas, with magnolias and camellias gorgeous in their season. I looked toward the sea again and lo! there was a sailing boat running before the wind toward the Bar from seaward. Anyone who had read the books would have no trouble in identifying one of those delightful two-masted topsail schooners which carried the slate from the port. I knew there were still two in existence, but I was much surprised to see one in sail. They were called the 'Western Ocean Yachts' and they were among the best built of all British sailing vessels: they had to be, or they could not survive based in a nasty corner of a nasty lee shore in Cardigan Bay, and so it proved.

There was a man in the crow's nest - a sort of barrel at the foremast head - and I could see him gesticulate to three others on the deck. There were a couple of slight alterations of her course but as she came in I could see no gap in the line of breakers facing her. As she ran into the breakers she pitched violently, and suddenly she struck the ground. The foremast snapped and dropped forwards, smashing the bowsprit in its fall. The man in the crow's nest was catapulted out in a graceful arc of waving arms and legs until he hit the surf: I did not see him again. Already the ebb tide and the incoming waves had seized the ship, slewed her round broadside to the sea, and rolled her on her beam ends. Within a minute she was under water on the port side and I could see the three men and two female figures - one larger than the other and doubtless the captain's wife and little daughter - trying to scramble into the shroads. The breakers struck them relentlessly and they were snatched away from the rigging into the sea one at a time; the child was last. I saw a dark spot bobbing in the water, and then no more. The schooner was sinking into the quicksands and disappeared bottom uppermost: it cannot have been more than three or four minutes since she struck, and still the incoming breakers met the strong ebb tide as if she had never been....

I was a little late for work: we were building the seaward side wall of the new carriage shops in Glan y Môr - a wall so long that it became known as Adrian's Wall.

'Where have you been?' they asked.

I told them, and there was a silence.

'Were they all drowned?' said someone.

'Oh, yes,' I said, 'all drowned, quite dead.'

'What?' said someone else, 'just now?'

A cloud passed from the face of the sun and chased up the Glaslyn valley toward Snowdon.

'No,' I said. 'It was all a hundred years ago.'

If thou must in this valley be
A century of Up and Down
Will never take thee once to see
The fair in Ludlow town.

What end to this eternal dream
But grind thy rails to dust?
And careless of thy motive power
Thy plates must fall to rust.

The hangman's cart, the soldier's tread
Will end in clay at break of dawn;
I'd rather pay my pound instead
And hear thy whistle greet the morn.

The Merionethshire Lad, ca.1900

The Smugglers of Portmeirion

veryone knows that the Welsh Sabbath is a day of compulsory sobriety. Anyone who would slake his thirst may hammer on the doors of licensed premises until the sound shall echo from the mountains, but answer shall not come. It is far better to go by stealth to G----m the Police, and say to him 'G----m, where can I get a drink?' And so it is that you come to steam your boots by the fire behind the bar parlour, where the local men, homeward bound from chapel politely pass the time of day. 'Quite all right it is,' they assure you, 'on a weekday we have the Pub, but on a Sunday we have the Club!'

It was not always so. In days gone by, there were no Clubs and law-abiding citizens had to buy their Sunday supplies upon the Saturday. You could see a row of women, homeward bound, each with her heavy-laden shopping bag emitting rhythmic clinks at every step. A proper lady would never thus betray her purpose - her bottles were well muffled in newspaper.

But shift the scene from the properly observed decorum of the coast to the mountain-circled boom town of Blaenau Ffestiniog. Here in days long gone were men whose thirst drank dry the vats by Saturday night, 'and look, man, the Lein Bach is shut on Sunday, so no more is to be had.' Who could resist the plight of men whose life was slate - born in a slate house, married in a slate chapel and buried under a slate tombstone? It was to meet the sad need of the miners of Blaenau the the Smugglers of Portmeirion arose.

The leader of this gang of desperadoes was Cadwaladr Casgen Cwrw[1], who like most of the other local brigands, claimed descent from Gruffydd ap Cynan, a Welsh warlord of the twelfth century. Cadwaladr's method was to ship liquor to the gunpowder anchorage each Saturday night, carry the crates ashore and load them into slate trucks. Beer was carried in bulk in the separate saddle tanks which were fitted over the years 1870 to 1890 to the small England engines for this purpose. The train, headed by the Bottom Shunting Engine, would rattle up to Blaenau, unload, and return in time for Chapel on Sunday morning.

The trouble started when the landlord of the Oakeley Arms was kept awake by the clinking of the passing bottles. Disliking this unfair competition, he and his cronies erected the Tank Trap which is still buried under the line between Tan y Bwlch and the Short Tunnel, and ambushed the train. Although after a hard fight the attackers were driven off and the train went on its way, some of the cargo was left behind. By morning, the Tylwyth Teg had been round, and all that Sunday the mountains were in an uproar with the carryings-on of tipsy fairies.

When the High Sheriff of Merioneth heard of this, he called out his posse (known, as you might expect, as the Men of Harlech) and decided to settle the trouble once and for all. He had the gate built across the line at Boston Lodge, arranged for it to be locked every Saturday night and the key to be kept in the General Manager's pocket. This flummoxed the smugglers, for though they were handy enough at managing boats and locomotives, they were quite hopeless at picking locks.

Their only remedy was to build a new railway and this was how the celebrated Glan y Môr and Portmeirion Railway began. It ran from the Glan y Môr yard behind the erecting shop, through the sand pit, and joined the main line of the F.R. just above Boston Lodge Station. The line was concealed in sand which was only dug out to allow the train to pass: this of course was the origin of the custom of ballasting the line up to the rail tops which was usual in those days.

When the trains ran again, the journeys developed into a series of running battles between the smugglers and the fairies, so the smugglers built a set of Armoured Liquor Wagons, one of which has survived as the F.R. Cement Van, No.16. This vehicle has armour outside and a wooden lining inside, so plainly it was built to repel external attack rather than to guard against internal explosion. Although it carried gunpowder at one stage in its career, it was not intended for this. The armoured trains were a great success and ran for many years. As times became quieter, the stock was augmented by a series of Fizzy

Pop Vans to keep Portmadoc Fire-Water, Cider and so on cool en route[2].

It was after the death of Cadwaladr Casgen Cwrw in 1903 that the decline set in. The Sunday liquor traffic, like so much else, ended because of road competition. Nowadays the beer is carried in great road tankers, disguised with the name 'Shell' or 'Mobil' on the side.

[1]Cadwallader the Barrel of Beer
[2]Down Empties Train (in Boyd, 1st ed'n Vol.II, p.208). In addition to the engine, the train consists of an Armoured Liquor Van, a F.R. truck used for empties (you can see a crate lid showing) and a Fizzy Pop Van. On the tender is the Barman in his white jacket.

The Fairlie

A Fairlie I should not advise -
With two of most things twice the size
It blows its ball-joints yearly.
However, should you feel inclined
To have one (to improve your mind
And not from fashion merely),
Then spend your lifetime underneath,
And when it kicks you in the teeth
Rebuild it, most severely.

I had a friend on Chili's coast,
Who kept a Fairlie for a boast
And ran it, for a bet:
He died, because the desert air
Both dried and fried the precious pair -
The Fairlie stands there yet.

attrib. 'The Bad Child's Book of Beasts' by Hilaire Belloc.

Linda & Blanche

It is difficult even now to hear an unbiassed description of the Great Penrhyn Slate Strike (or Lock-Out) of 1900-03. Historians contradict each other with academic venom almost as vigorously as the quarrymen and their families quarrelled nearly a hundred years ago. Doubtless there were faults on both sides: however, this story comes from the local Welsh accounts and cannot be regarded as wholly impartial.

nce upon a time there was a slate quarry. It was a very large quarry, in fact it was the largest slate quarry in the world, but it was not a very happy quarry. It was at Bethesda near Bangor in Caernarvonshire, and the men made a living digging the purple slate from the hillside and sending it down the little railway to Port Penrhyn to be sent in sailing boats and sometimes steam ships to build the roofs of the houses in Liverpool and Manchester, not to mention many other towns as well.

The quarry was owned by the wicked Lord Penrhyn. Slate owners live for ever, and they lived in as grand a style as they could. Look at the house of the Oakeleys at Plas Tan y Bwlch: it is very grand, like a railway station, and it is by no means the biggest of the slate-owners' residences. The grandest of them all was Penrhyn Castle, where George Sholto Douglas Pennant, the wicked Baron Penrhyn, lived. He also had rather a grand house in the middle of London and a grand estate in the English countryside near Bletchley in Buckinghamshire. He thought he was a very good baron, but his workers thought he was a very bad baron indeed. He was lean and he was mean, he was mad and he was bad, and he lived off the back of his workers in the slate quarry. He made a profit of a hundred thousand pounds a year out of his quarry, and his three thousand workmen were lucky if they could take home three pounds a week apiece, and many of them took a lot less.

Lord Penrhyn had an agent, Mr Emilius Alexander Young. Mr Young was an accountant, and his job was to make sure the workmen quarried the slate for as little money as could be managed. Mr Young was a keen cyclist, and he rode about the district to Betws y Coed and Conway on Lord Penrhyn's affairs, as most of the district belonged to Lord Penrhyn anyway. Lord Penrhyn's son Edward Sholto was member of parliament for Caernarvon County, so the troubles of the quarrymen were not likely to be questioned in the House of Commons. Lord Penrhyn had an electricity power station in the quarry, and any electricity which was left over from the quarry was sold for use in Bethesda: this was thought very up to date at the time. Lord Penrhyn had friends and relations in the Government, and he knew all the right people.

His workmen didn't: they mostly spoke Welsh and if they got as far as Bangor occasionally, that was as far as they went. They went to chapel twice on Sundays and listened to sermons about Sin and the Dangers of Falling into the Pit. As the Pit in the Quarry was about a thousand feet from top to bottom, they knew what the Parch was preaching about, even if they were not too sure about Sin.

One day there was trouble at the quarry. The quarrymen worked by bargains: that is, they agreed with Mr Young to dig out so much slate for a month for a certain price. Mr Young gave the best bargains to the ones he liked best, being the ones who went to church instead of chapel. Mr Young would give no work at all to a thousand of the quarrymen, so the other two thousand refused to work unless he changed his mind. Mr Young turned them all out of the quarry and locked the gate. The Great Lock-Out (or strike) went on for three years and it still holds the record for the longest strike (or lock-out) in Britain.

The power station at the quarry was closed down so that nobody in Bethesda had any electricity. When people looked sullen at Mr Emilius Young, Lord Penrhyn had his friends in the Government send three hundred soldiers to frighten them. This did him no good: the local people made friends with the soldiers, who went away again in high good humour. There was very little other work in Bethesda, so many of the families were very hard up. They hardly had enough to eat: a thousand men left the district to work in coal mines in South Wales, or to find jobs in England. Four choirs of quarrymen went to England and even to America to sing for a living, and because in those days there was no television and very little in the way of cinemas, lots of people went to hear them and sent money to help their families in Bethesda. When the Board of Trade asked if it could help to settle the strike, Lord Penrhyn said it was entirely his private affair: when the Board of Trade replied that several thousand starving families was a matter of public interest, Lord Penrhyn would have none of it.

Feelings in Bethesda became very sour. Some of the men were so short of food that they had to go back to work when the quarry was reopened, and to encourage them, Lord Penrhyn offered a golden sovereign to those who would return. Their workmates still on strike called them *bradwyr* - traitors - and the town was divided bitterly for years. One woman took a golden sovereign to show her neighbour.

'Look what my man got for going back,' she said.

Her neighbour spat 'Judas was only paid in silver!'

They never spoke to each other again.

A local trade union official declared that Lord Penrhyn had even reduced the price of treachery - from thirty pieces of silver to twenty. Lord Penrhyn sued him for libel, and, in a court conducted in English, of course he won.

The only bright spot in this unhappy state of affairs was that Edward Sholto's wife did not approve of her father-in-law's behaviour. Her name was Blanche, and she was joined by her daughter Linda - who was twelve at the time - in taking baskets of groceries to the families of the quarrymen, no matter who they were. So the quarrymens' families did not actually starve, however near they came to it.

Ever afterwards, the locomotives on the little railway to Port Penrhyn which carried the names of *Blanche* and *Linda* were kept in apple-pie order and most impeccably clean by the men who ran the little railway.

So that is why when Allan Garraway was looking for locomotives for the Ffestiniog Railway, he came across these two beautiful little engines on the Penrhyn Quarry Railway.

They say that the engine called *Lord Penrhyn* went for scrap many long years ago.

George Sholto Gordon Douglas Pennant (1836 - 1907) 2nd Baron Penrhyn whose son was Edward Sholto Douglas Pennant (1864 - 1927) 3rd Baron Penrhyn, who married Blanche Georgiana Fitzroy (1865 - 1944) and they had a daughter Linda Blanche Douglas Pennant (1889 - 1965).

ENGINES

Fairlie of Ffestiniog from distant Llyn Ystradau,
Cruising in the evening down the permanent way,
Showing off the mountains,
Lakes and rhododendrons,
With a golden seaward sunset at the close of day.

Sturdy Snowdon Switzer with a canvas-windowed carriage,
Grinding up the rack through the sheep-nibbled grass,
Looking down on scree slopes,
Cliff tops, slate tips,
And covering the summit with cans and broken glass.

Dirty British Railways with a soot-caked smokebox,
Blasting up the Rheidol in the holiday peak;
Setting light to haystacks,
Forestry and farmsteads,
Calling out the fire brigade seven days a week.

in the manner of John Masefield (1878 - 1967)

THREE MEN AND A Dragon

Once upon a time in the Good Old Days there was a red dragon called Caradoc. He was useful at Boston Lodge lighting up the locomotives because his breath was so hot. He ate the scraps from the fitters' packed lunches in the Den, and he slept in the smithy on a pile of Black Diamonds which he had collected for himself. But the price of Black Diamonds went up and up, and so did the number of forest fires because the engines had to work harder pulling all the people who came to ride on the railway.

One day Paul the Works Manager came to Caradoc and told him 'Get off those coals, Caradoc, there's another job for you. Coal is out, Caradoc, and the engines are going to drink Perfume of Araby instead.'

'Whatever's that?' asked Caradoc, and went to look.

Perfume of Araby was a greasy brown liquid like runny treacle and it smiled at you in a slimy kind of way.

Now,' said Paul, 'Caradoc, you just blow down this pipe,' and Caradoc had to hoosh hot air into *Linda* to squirt the Perfume of Araby into her firebox until she boiled. Caradoc would much rather hoosh flames into a well laid fire of Black Diamonds. Blowing down the pipe made him go blue in the face, which is most undignified for Red Dragons. But the forest fires stopped, and things were rather cleaner, so Caradoc put up with it all.

But then the price of Perfume of Araby went up and up too, so the railway took anything from candle ends to naphtha and put it all in an enormous tank. Everything seethed and simmered inside, then they ran the mixture through a tea

Caradoc's feeding bottle

strainer to get the nuts and bolts out, and tried burn the results in the locomotives. It was all right in the winter and even warmed *Mountaineer* somewhat, but in the summer it made *Linda* and *Blanche* cough so they couldn't pull the trains so well. And something gave Caradoc terrible tummy-ache: he could not be sure whether it was the taste of the candle ends or the poor quality of the leavings from the fitters' packed lunches.

Times grew harder, the fitters grew thinner and thinner, and there were no leavings at all from the packed lunches in the new Amenity Block. Caradoc did not get enough to eat and he could not blow the pipe any more. So they put in an air compressor and poor Caradoc was out of a job.

'Economy,' said Paul, 'I'm very sorry, Caradoc, but we are told to save every penny. But you could always join the Deviation,' he added, 'they tell me things are better up there.'

So Caradoc took his hoard of black diamonds with him up to the Deviation and he lived there on porridge, tinned peaches and cider. He tried dry stone walling, at which he was very bad, and rock blasting at which he was much better because his breath was so hot. The trouble was that the Deviationists only worked at weekends so all week Caradoc slept on his pile of coals. One working weekend he overslept and the Deviationists covered him in a great heap of stones. When times are bad, dragons can sleep for years, you see, and wake up when times are better.

So Caradoc slept for some years though every now and then the Welsh rain would trickle down his neck and he would turn over, making the rocks slide down the embankment and chasing away the dry stone wallers at the bottom.

Time went by and the Deviationists began to build the New Tunnel. The rock was very hard and very tricky, and the Three Miners came to drill it. They were called Bob and Robin and Pete, and they drilled a hole into the mountain eight feet high, eight feet wide and eight feet long. What with stones falling on their heads at the entrance and the granite inside, they had a hard time of it, so they went off with Bunny Lewis to think what to do.

'Black Powder' said Bob.

'Doesn't work' said Pete.

'Jelly' said Robin.

'Doesn't work' said Bob.

'Dynamite' said Pete.

'Doesn't work' said Robin.

'You could always ask Caradoc,' said Bunny. 'He's a dragon,' he explained, 'he sleeps under a pile of stones, and he was quite good at blasting when he was with us before.'

So the Three Miners went up the hill to Dragon Bank.

'Caradoc,' they cried, 'wake up. Caradoc,' they shouted. 'come out!'

A red and bleary head stuck out from the stones, steaming faintly. He didn't mean to, you understand; it was just because his breath was so hot.

'Caradoc,' they said, 'we've got work for you!'

So Caradoc the dragon went with the Three Miners into Tunnel Newydd, and he blasted and he flamed, and he fumed and he smoked until even the Three Miners had to go outside for fresh air. Then he scrabbled and he scraped and he scrummaged and he shovelled all the rocks into skips for the Three Miners to take away. The only trouble was that he cracked all the rocks around the tunnel right through the mountain. He didn't mean to, you understand, it was just that his breath was so hot. So the Three Miners decided that the Tunnel Newydd had to be lined with concrete, and Bunny was called.

'Here, Caradoc,' he said, 'have a drink and squirt this wet concrete up into the roof so it sticks there. There's a good dragon, just drink some wet concrete and get real stoned.'

Caradoc tried it. It tasted disgusting.

'Ugh!', said he. 'This stuff cools me down too much. It puts my fire out. I don't mind volunteering for things,' he remarked, 'but this stuff isn't safe for dragons.'

The railway directors heard about it: they offered him danger money.

'Not for me, thank you,' replied Caradoc politely, 'but it wouldn't be worth the pay you get on this railway. So I'm going back to my coal hole at Dragon Bank. You can come and fetch me when you find another job I can do. What you need for squirting wet concrete,' he added over his shoulder, 'is an elephant.'

So off he went. The Company had to have a lot of men to finish the Tunnel Newydd, and it took a lot longer than it had with Three Men and a Dragon.

And Caradoc? He is still asleep on his hoard of Black Diamonds under Cei Ddraig, and if the train tiptoes very carefully over his head, you will understand why. And if a few stones slide down the hill on a wet day, it is only because Caradoc turns over when the Welsh rain trickles down his neck.

SPENT COALS

I

Trains present and trains past
Are both perhaps present in trains future,
And trains future contained in trains past.
If all trains are eternally present,
All trains must be in the timetable.
What might have been is no abstraction
But a reality eternally present
In a factual world of speculation.
Points at both ends of a section
Awaiting trains future in time present
Eternally waiting for time in the table
Unreal on the printed page, ever present
From nine-thirty Up to nine-thirty Down.
At night there are only trains past and trains future
So therefore all time is suspended:
Let us come to the point.
All time must come to the point,

For all trains must pass between points:
Down trains arrive at Up points in time past
And Up trains depart from the same in time future.
The red and green lights which reflect in the rails
Are eternally present:
There they are, dignified, invisible away from the point,
Moving towards and away from the trains.
In the autumn heat, through the vibrant air,
The unseen music of trains in the shrubbery:
Quick, called the bird, the trains are full of children
Hidden excitedly, laughing in trains in the woods.
Trains present and trains past
What might have been and what has been
Have points at the end, which are always present.

II

Fish the bullhead in the mud
Grease the seized-up axle tree
Telegraph wires in the blood
Sing beside the antique cars
Taking ghosts to ancient wars.
They pass beneath the rowan tree
And see through glass the many stars.
Ascend in autumn to the tree
And sweep aside the fallen leaf
To hear upon the sodden ground

The ballast tamper's deadened sound
While wearied volunteers stand round
Their heads are filled with many stars.

III

The train descending fills the air
With flames of incandescent steel,
And gathers past to future, where
The still point of the turning wheel
Gilds the crankpin in its poise -
The dancing orbit time destroys
And time is eternally present.
A moment's life of fiery breath
And cooling ash returns to earth;
Ash on a fireman's sleeve
Is all the ash the spent coals leave;
Dust in the air suspended
Marks the spot where the journey ended.
The future's echoing footsteps sound
Quick said the bird; here, now, always -
The pound and the Prince are one:
Eternally present.

poss. attrib. T. S. Eliot?

"Blerum, blerum, blerum," sang Heinin.

Taliesin

1. Ceridwen

n times long past there lived a man called Tegid Foel, and he dwelt in the depths of Llyn Tegid. So the tale begins, but there is more to this: Tegid is the Welsh form of the Latin Tacitus, which means the Silent One, and Moel or Foel is the name for a round bald mountain with no trees on the top. Llyn Tegid is Lake Bala, which lies in a deep valley between the Berwyn and Arenig Mountains. So apart from saying Tegid was called Hill and lived in a Lake, you could say he was bald and owned a lot of land around Bala. You lose bits in the cracks between the Welsh, the Latin and the English. The rest of the tale is just the same, but it would all take too long to explain.

Tegid had a wife called Ceridwen; she was no beauty but she had other qualities. Depending on how you look at things, she was either a Celtic goddess or a very powerful witch. In either case the worry was quite enough to drive Tegid bald.

They had three children: Morfran was a strong lad who went off to King Arthur's court to be a knight, and Creirwy was such an uncommonly good-looking young lady that she is mentioned in the Triads as one of the Three Beauties of the Island of Britain. Ceridwen was very pleased with the pair of them and thought they were well set up for life, but the third....oh dear. He was the ugliest boy you ever saw; he was clumsy and thick into the bargain. His name was Afagddu which means Black Face, and if you guess that meant he couldn't be bothered to shave most mornings, perhaps you're right. But unattractive as he was, Ceridwen worried about his future, as mothers do. How could she make him fit for polite society? She could never make him as beautiful as Creirwy nor could she make him as strong and deft as Morfran. Perhaps she could make him wise and maybe even able to see into the future, and then maybe King Arthur would be glad to see him at court. She took her

77

Bumper Book of Spells and found a recipe.

It was very difficult: she had to gather all sorts of herbs at the right season of the year and boil them in a pot for a year and a day. So she got out the Cauldron of Inspiration and Knowledge and put it on the fire. As she didn't want anyone to know what she was up to, she set a blind man called Morda to stir it, and she needed somebody ordinary to fetch the wood and top up the water, so she sent for the most extraordinarily ordinary boy she knew, who was Little Gwion from Llanfair Caereinion.

So Ceridwen went out about Arenig and Berwyn and Aran Benllyn looking for herbs for the pot, while Morda solemnly stirred it and Little Gwion went about the extraordinarily ordinary tasks of fetching firewood, chopping sticks or carrying cans of water. Now and then there would be moments of excitement when Ceridwen came back by Crosville bus from Castell Carndochan or somewhere with more herbs. Often enough the pot smelt terrible and made their eyes sting. This went on through the seasons for a year, and at the end of a year and a day Afagddu didn't want to come near the pot which smelt so bad, so he went and hid. Ceridwen went to find him, as mothers will, and while she was looking, the cauldron spat and three drops of hot liquid landed on Gwion's finger.

'Ouch!' he said, and stuck his finger in his mouth. Then he suddenly realised that he knew everything that had been, everything that is and everything that was to happen. It only took a moment to realise that Ceridwen would be unpleasant when she got back: he had seen enough of her moods in the last year and a day to know her ways.

The best thing, he thought, would be to go back to Llanfair Caereinion as fast as he could, so he set off to run across the fields up towards the Berwyn. He had gone half a mile when he heard a fearful rumpus from the house, and saw Ceridwen coming after him. She was in a terrible temper, so she ran very fast, and was catching him up.

'I wish I could go faster,' panted Gwion, 'like a hare!'

To his surprise he found he was much closer to the ground, with four furry legs and long ears. He ran much faster, over the Berwyn down to Llangynog when he looked over his shoulder and there behind him was the most enormous black hound you ever saw with great teeth and its tongue hanging out. Gwion jumped into the river.

'I wish I was a fish,' he thought, and lo and behold, he was a salmon. He swam down the Afon Tanat, but looking over his shoulder, to his horror he saw a black otter with red eyes gaining on him. He jumped out of the river in a fright.

'I wish I was a bird, a great big bird,' he thought, and lo and behold, he was

a large and croaking raven. He flew over the hill but just as he came to Welshpool, he saw a black hawk above, about to attack him. He landed rapidly, of course at Raven Square. There he found the Llanfair Jinny about to depart, so he turned back into himself, bought a single ticket to Llanfair Caereinion and got on the train. With all these other people from Llanfair about, he thought, surely there could be no more trouble.

When they reached the Cyfronydd lane crossing, the guard looked back in puzzlement.

'I thought we were the only train on the line today,' he said, 'but I'm sure I heard something behind us.'

Presently as they crossed the Banwy Bridge, they saw an awful sight behind them: a great black engine with *two* chimneys pounding along behind them. They only just reached Llanfair Caereinion before it caught up with them. Gwion jumped out of the train, hid in the goods shed, turned himself into a grain of wheat and went to sleep. He was exhausted.

While he slept, a black hen came into the goods shed and pecked around until it found him and ate him. Then Ceridwen (for it was she) clucked and went back home.

Now, either Celtic goddesses manage matters otherwise than we do, or the people who first told this tale were not so well informed as we are, because the story tells us that nine months later Ceridwen had a baby, as people do. He was a very beautiful baby, but Afagddu would have it that he was really Little Gwion in disguise.

'Enough trouble last time,' he said, 'I don't want that all over again!'

There was quite a family row and Tegid suggested they had the baby fostered, which was a usual thing in Wales in those days.

'Anything for a quiet life,' he sighed.

But the baby would still be part of the family, so Afagddu made a terrible fuss: he would raise an army or at any rate a gang of teenagers and rebel against his father if the baby stayed. As the saying goes, better the province than the prince, so the baby had to go.

They put the beautiful baby in a little coracle, a leathern boat on a willow frame, and put him in the river at Drws y Nant to float down the stream. But Ceridwen had a private word with the water nymph Mawddach, who promised to take good care of her treasured child. And all this took place at the end of April, many years ago.

2. Elphin

Gwyddno Garanhir was King of the Lowland Hundred. It was the best land in Wales, and stretched from Portmadoc and Barmouth miles to the west. The Afon Glaslyn meandered peacefully through the grazing cattle and the fields of waving golden corn. Port Gwyddno was one of the three greatest harbours of Wales. It was all very prosperous; Gwyddno hunted and shot and fished, composed decent poetry, ran the courts - not that there was much trouble - kept out neighbouring warlords who fancied the Lowland Hundred, gathered the taxes and generally lived the life of a respectable prince with decent wine coming in Tintagel B ware from the Mediterranean in his own ships to his own port. He ate with silver and he drank from gold.

Because the land was low, it was set around with sea-walls and dykes to keep out the sea and the mermaid Gwenhidwy who had been displaced when

the dykes were built. The dykes were in the charge of Seithennyn who was *Arglwydd Argae*, which you could say meant Lord Keeper of the Cob. He drew the Cob Duties, and lived in a high old style as grand as that of his King; he left his duties to his assistants, who left it to the lengthmen, who grazed cattle, gathered sloes and blackberries on the sides of the Cob and otherwise did nothing.

Gwyddno had a son Elphin, an amiable young man with an unfortunate tendency to get into trouble for telling the truth indiscreetly. The truth is often inconvenient for people in powerful places, so Prince Elphin, though a thoroughly decent man, lived in rather a poor way. He had married the fair Angharad, Seithennyn's daughter, and they lived at Abermawddach - or Barmouth if you will - some miles from the end of the Cob at Mochras. There was a fish-weir at Barmouth, and Elphin had a sort of time-share there; he had the profit of the catch from it each May Eve.

One May Day dawn, Elphin was watching his catch at the fish weir, and to his great disappointment, there was hardly a thing. He had hoped to have a vast catch to sell, because being honest, he had very little money, and at least he thought he could take a salmon home to eat, but no. A few crabs and the odd flounders. Well, flounders were delicious and still are, but they don't make your fortune.

The water nymph Mawddach was taking good care not to be seen, but at the very end of the waters coming through the sluice in the weir came a little black thing, and when it came closer, there was a little leathern boat on a wicker frame, with a beautiful baby boy in it, dressed in the very best kind of baby clothes and gold thread woven in the edge of his blankets.

'There,' said the fishermen, 'a son for you, lord Elphin!' because he hadn't been married long enough to have any of his own. Elphin looked glum: the fishermen didn't realise how hard up he was and here was another mouth to feed (In the light of what happened afterwards, a Welsh saying grew up - 'as glum as Elffin on finding Taliesin'). But the baby smiled, so being a decent soul, Elphin took up the coracle and the contents and took them home.

Angharad was delighted.

'What a fair brow *(Tal iesin)* he has!' she cried.

And so the child was named. He grew up not only good-looking, but intelligent and studious. Perhaps he was a little lacking in the feats of strength of the other boys, but he could get things done by his ingenuity in devising tools to do heavy jobs for him. He proved good at the literary skills: Gwyddno took him in hand to teach him the arts of poetry, at which he soon surpassed his master. When he was about ten or twelve years old, Taliesin took an interest in engineering, and one September weekend Elphin took him to see the sea-walls

and dykes around the Lowland Hundred.

They found the sluices rotten, the watercourses choked with brambles, the dykes subsiding and the cobs extensively cracked.

They stayed the night with Seithennyn at his castle on the edge of the sea, ten miles west of Mochras.

Elphin, as ever, was injudicious in what he said at table.

'Lord Seithennyn,' he said, 'we have looked at the works to keep the waters out of the Lowland Hundred, and they are much in need of repair.'

'Oh, no, my lad,' smiled Seithennyn over the edge of his golden goblet. 'They were good enough in my grandfather's time and they will be good enough in my grandson's. Cupbearer, fill my goblet.'

'But the sluices are rotten, and the dykes are subsiding,' insisted Elphin.

'Parts of the walls are excellent,' said Seithennyn.

'I wish it were all so,' Elphin answered.

'No,' said Seithennyn. 'If it were all solid, it would be too rigid. You need a certain flexibility in works against the sea. So the rotten parts are more elastic, and save the solid works from damage in the time of storms. In any case, there have been no serious storms for over a hundred years. The climate grows warmer, and the storms are the less. Our forefathers knew what they were about; they built the walls to protect us, and Heaven forbid that we should meddle with their handiwork. Cupbearer, this wine is excellent. Fill my goblet!'

'But the walls are no longer in a state to protect us' urged Elphin, 'and all the farmers of the Lowland Hundred are at risk because of your complacency. Your duty is to protect the people, and yet you do nothing to keep up the old dykes.'

'That the dykes are old is a fact of life,' replied Seithennyn. 'That they are rotten, I might, for the sake of old friendship, agree. That they are any the worse for that, I would argue most strongly against you. It is impossible for us to improve on the works of olden times. Their immortal work has stood for centuries and will stand for centuries more if we let it alone. Cupbearer, fill....'

'Yet the level of the sea has risen since those days,' objected Elphin. 'The dykes should be built higher.'

'How can the level of the sea alter?' laughed Seithennyn. ' I can alter the level of the wine in this goblet, but how can anyone alter the level of the sea? Cupbearer, fill!'

'Seithennyn,' said Elphin, 'even though you are my father-in-law, I am horrified that you stand and defend your neglect of duty. I shall have to speak to my father of what I have seen.'

'Stand!' cried Seithennyn, 'who said anything about standing?'

So he stood up, and fell flat on his back.

'The wine speaks, even in the absence of reason' murmured Taliesin quietly into Elphin's ear.

That night was the time of the equinoctial spring tides, and a great storm blew up. The sea crashed against the castle walls and shook them. In the darkest part of the night, Elphin felt a hand shake his arm: it was Taliesin.

'My lord,' whispered the boy,'I can see the castle falling in the sea and the land drowning. I can see the mermaid Gwenhidwy calling up the winds.'

Elphin got out of bed and looked into the blackness of the night.

'You see more than I,' he grumbled as he struck a light.

Taliesin's face was pale.

'Lord Elphin, let us leave at once. We shall lose our lives if we stay here.'

Something about the boy's intensity persuaded Elphin, and the pair packed their bag and went down to the gatehouse. Scarcely had they done so when the tower they had just left collapsed with a loud noise into the raging sea. The Cob cracked and broke; and as the sea poured inland, Taliesin saw the triumphant wave of a victorious mermaid's tail: it was the return of Gwenhidwy.

Seithennyn appeared, red-eyed and waving a sword.

'Where is the enemy?' he cried.

'There is no enemy except the sea,' replied Elphin, 'and against that your sword is powerless. Do you not hear the cries of the people in the Lowland Hundred, who have left their protection to you? They drown, and they are cursing you as they die!'

'Show me the enemy!' shouted Seithennyn, and ran to face the waves. Elphin turned from him is despair.

'There is nothing more we can do here, lord,' said Taliesin, 'but we can save ourselves by walking along the top of the Cob back to Mochras, supposing it is not broken elsewhere.'

So they set out with spears in their hands to help them stand against the force of the wind, and as day broke they found themselves clambering along the top of the Cob with the sea spray splashing them on both sides while they looked at the wreck of the Lowland Hundred.

If you look out from Mochras you can still see nine miles of the old Cob wall reaching out to the west. People say Saint Patrick once tried to walk to Ireland that way: he failed, but the old Cob is still called Sarn Badrig, Saint Patrick's Causeway.

3. Maelgwn

Gwyddno and most of his people were lost in this disaster, and Elphin found himself the ruler of a small remnant of his people. The other local warlords had a fine time ravaging his belongings because he could no longer call up armies from the Lowland Hundred to defend him, but fortunately Taliesin was very acute at seeing enemies coming in good time to take cover in caves in the hills of Ardudwy.

After the death of King Arthur, Maelgwn Gwynedd who was the local warlord to the north, became the king in name and one time he and his followers descended the hills of Ardudwy in pursuit of a stag, which they killed on Elphin's doorstep. It is of course a fearful insult for a nobleman to kill another nobleman's stag in this manner. Elphin was away from home at the time, and Taliesin had warned Angharad and the household in time, so they had hidden among the rocks. Maelgwn's men set about cooking the stag on Elphin's fire, and they ate it at his table, washing it down with his wine and beer. At this stage, Elphin, all unsuspecting, returned home and was taken prisoner. Maelgwn decided that he had better repay Elphin's involuntary hospitality by taking him, against his protests, to the fortress of Deganwy, where he did at least invite Elphin to a feast. It was a feast such as Elphin had not seen since the loss of the Lowland Hundred, and the courtiers were loud in their creeping crawling praise of the generosity of their king, the beauty and the virtue of their queen, the marvellous performance of the king's bards and the grace and speed of the king's horses: all the flatteries which a vain tyrant likes to hear. Now Maelgwn had murdered his own nephew so that he could marry the nephew's wife: this was

the virtuous queen being praised. Maybe Elphin had a glass or two too many of Maelgwn's excellent wine and could not keep a bridle on his tongue.

'My wife is better looking than the queen, with or without her clothes on, and more virtuous too,' said Elphin.

Everyone looked horrified.

'Anything else?' inquired Maelgwn, with deceptive calm.

'No, not much,' Elphin replied. 'Except of course that my bard is much better than yours, and my horse is faster.'

'Take him away!' bawled Maelgwn, in a sudden temper. 'Put him in chains and give him bread and water in the foulest dungeon we have in the castle!'

Then just as suddenly recovering his temper, he added in an oily way: 'But as he is a gentleman, would you be so kind as to make sure you load him with the *silver* chains? And do make sure he has the *best* wheat bread to eat....'

As the guards removed a protesting Elphin, Maelgwn looked round his court with a nasty smile. His eye lit on a stocky young man who had two young women on his knee.

'Rhûn,' he said. 'Come here. The good Prince Elphin has a most virtuous wife, he says. You have a certain way with virtuous ladies, haven't you? Now you just go to Elphin's place and make sure the ladies are cared for, won't you? And don't come back until you have good evidence that there is more virtue in this court than in his, will you?' He stroked his own long moustaches lovingly.

A challenge of this sort was just what Rhûn enjoyed, so he set out for Ardudwy. He was met by a respectful teenage boy who showed him into the hall, where he was received by a rather frowzy lady with coarse hands, attended by a tall maidservant who looked down her nose at him and slammed the food on the table.

'It's a good job I haven't got to impress the maid,' he thought.

Rhûn had a simple way with ladies: he tanked them up with wine or beer until they went to sleep and then he Had His Way with them. In this case he didn't fancy the frowzy lady; so when she went to sleep he just cut off her little finger which had a large signet ring on it, and decamped back to Deganwy. Maelgwn was delighted. He had Elphin brought in his tinkling silver chains from the dungeon and sat him at his table.

'Have a drink, Lord Elphin', sneered Maelgwn. 'You'll need it, because here is your ring, is it not? And look, it is still on your virtuous wife's finger!'

He laughed, and Rhûn simpered and nodded. Elphin was shaken, but he had been brought up carefully in legal matters in the courts of his father Gwyddno.

'Always examine all the evidence, and let everybody say everything they want,' Gwyddno had insisted.

Elphin made Rhûn describe everybody he had met at Elphin's hall in Ardudwy. His spirits rose.

'The ring is mine: that is my seal upon it,' he said at length, and Maelgwn relaxed in pleasure.

'However,' continued Elphin. 'That is not my wife's finger. The finger is too thick: my wife has thin fingers. That ring is meant to be worn over my wife's glove. It is meant for people to kiss her hand in public. Well,' he said as Maelgwn looked dubious,'would *you* let just anybody kiss your wife's bare hand? You never know what she might catch.'

Maelgwn looked embarrassed, because he *hadn't* thought of that.

'Next,' continued Elphin, 'my wife cuts her fingernails every Saturday night. This nail hasn't been cut for a month. And furthermore,' he said, getting out a magnifying glass, 'there is rye dough under the nail, My wife hasn't kneaded the dough since I married her, and if she has to nowadays, even in the state you have reduced us to, she would never have kneaded *rye* dough. Why, you give me wheat bread even in prison. Besides,' he added in his usual truthful way, 'if you should ever be invited to dine with my wife, which I doubt, you will find she has all her fingers.'

'Take him away,' said Maelgwn in a tone of frustrated fury, and as the guards led him out, Elphin heard Maelgwn turn with a roar on the incompetent Rhûn.

Taliesin was growing up. After spotting the arrival of Rhûn and arranging for Angharad and the maid to change places, he felt guilty because the maid had lost her little finger. Something must be done; he must rescue his master Elphin, so he sought leave of absence from Angharad, saddled his little pony, took his toothbrush and his bag of poems, and set out for Deganwy. When he arrived at Maelgwn's court, he knocked at the gate.

'What do you do?' asked the sergeant of the guard.

'I'm a bard,' replied Taliesin, waving his bag of odes.

Now there were three classes of bard.

First there were wandering bards who went from place to place telling stories, singing songs and bringing the latest gossip, who were welcome everywhere they went for the gossip if nothing else. Second there were household bards who lived with the nobler families and who also helped with the education of the children. Lastly, most highly regarded and deeply respected were the Head Bards, who had served their time in bardic schools and were masters of their craft: they knew everybody's ancestors back to Adam and they knew all matters artistic and scientific.

So a wandering bard was welcome.

'Come in,' said the sergeant. 'Sit at the bottom of the table over there behind the pillar, and I'll see you get enough to eat. You can tell me the news later.'

Dinner was duly served, and afterwards the king's Head Bards, Idno and Heinin, were summoned to praise the king's valour, justice and generosity. This made Taliesin cross, considering that Elphin was chained in the cellar, so as Heinin passed him on the way into the hall, Taliesin flipped his finger across his lips, and when Heinin raised his voice in song, all that came out was the noise of a child blowing bubbles with its mouth.

'Blerum, blerum, blerum,' sang Heinin. Thrice he stopped and thrice he started again, and each time was more foolish than before.

Maelgwn banged his goblet on the table and spilt his wine.

'Heinin, you drunken fool,' he hissed. 'How often do I have tell you to leave the wine until after you've sung?'

'I'm not drunk, so please your majesty. There's an evil spirit at work.' Heinin looked around, saw Taliesin's unguarded smile and cried out.

'Your majesty, there he is! That lad, grinning behind the pillar!'

Maelgwn looked a bit doubtful.

'Come out here, lad,' he said, not unkindly. 'Tell me who you are, and what you do.'

He little expected Taliesin's reply. According to the story, it was a bardic ode which has rung through history since, and has made Taliesin's name immortal.

Head Chief Bard am I to Elphin,
My original country was the land of the summer stars;
Idno and Heinin called me Merddin,
At length every king shall call me Taliesin.

I was with the angels, at the fall of Lucifer,
I have borne a banner, in front of Alexander,
I know the names of stars, from the north to south,
I was on the galaxy, at the throne from whence they came.
I was in Canaan when Absalom was murdered,
I was master mason, when we built the tower of Babel,
I was in India, when Rome was first constructed.
I have now come hither, with the relics of the Trojans.
I was at the court of Don, before the birth of Gwydion;
I have been three times imprisoned by Arianrhod.
I am a wonder with an unknown beginning.

I had no father, I had no mother,
I was made from earth and clay,
And blessed with nine senses,
Coming from fruits and from roots,
Of primroses, flowers from the hills,
Of tree and bush bloom
Of nettle blossom and the spume
Of the ninth wave's foam.

Then I was for nine months
Inside the witch Ceridwen:
At first I was little Gwion,
But at last I am Taliesin.

Maelgwn and his court didn't understand it at all, but it was new and they hadn't heard it before, and he could plainly do better than Idno and Heinin, so they cheered.

'What do you want for your bard-fee?' asked Maelgwn.

'Elphin's liberty,' replied Taliesin boldly.

Maelgwn paused for quite a long time and tapped his finger several times quietly on the table.

'Were it not for the inviolability of person laid on bards,' he said slowly in an evil voice, 'I would kill you for that. However, answer me: why I should let him go?'

Taliesin had no mind to get into an argument with the king.

'Let me ask you this instead,' he said.

What is the thing from before the flood,
No flesh, no bone,
No vein, no blood,
No trunk, no head.
No hand, no foot.
Neither older nor younger
Nor with the signs of old age
Though it lasts through the years without number?
How the sea whitens when it comes!
Great is the damage it causes on coasts!
It is in the field, in the wood,
It was not born, nor can it be seen.
It comes from four quarters
No king can confine it.
It is wet, it is dry,
It is mild, it is strong,
It is silent, can sing,
It is the noisiest thing.
It is good, it is bad,
It is calm, it is mad.
It has been made, apart from all creatures
To wreak justice and vengeance on Maelgwn Gwynedd!

As Taliesin sang this riddle, the answer became apparent; as he sang, the wind arose, first as a gentle breeze, and then stiffening into a howling gale which broke the castle windows, blew everyone to the floor, smashed the furniture and shook the whole place so that it felt as if it were about to blow down.

Maelgwn couldn't make himself heard, and if he had opened his mouth the wind would have blown him backwards. He signed to the guards to fetch Elphin, and when he was with difficulty brought, the wind blew the silver chains off him and the gale suddenly stopped.

You would have thought Elphin would have been glad enough to get out of Deganwy Castle alive and go home, but he was never one to leave unfinished business.

'King Maelgwn,' said he, 'there is the matter of the horses between us.'

With an ill grace, Maelgwn agreed to have a horse race on Conwy Morfa, though he must have known in his heart that he would lose the race and a lot of money on the betting. Of course, he did, so Elphin had a large bag of money won at horse-racing.

Just as the horse race ended, Elphin's jockey dropped his cap.

'Dig here,' said Taliesin, and they dug up a great pot of treasure.

'This is for you, lord Elphin,' said Taliesin. 'It's fair payment *(tal iesin)* for bringing me up.'

And according to the old tale, they all lived happily for many long years afterwards.

More; if you believe some people, Taliesin is still with us.

93

envoi

What was that? Nothing.

Nothing but the cotton grass blown in the mire
By the wind that whistles in a rusted wire
Or hums like the draught of a long dead fire -

What was that? Nothing.

Nothing but the sigh of a cylinder drain
The departed rumble of a long gone train
Or the tinkling of sliding slate in the rain -

What was that? Nothing.

Nothing but the stumble of boots in the clay
Of the bed of the rushes where the sleepers lay
In the green ruination of the permanent way -

What was that? Nothing.

Artwork, origination and typesetting by
David Charlesworth, Notions by Design, 151 Moorland View Road,
Chesterfield, Derbyshire. S4O 3DD
First published 1994.

Published by the Festiniog Railway Company, Portmadog

ISBN 0 901848 08 5